# Get Into Your Body
## LEVEL 1: THE WORKBOOK

# The Ixchel System
## VICTORIA JAHKELINE SALOMON

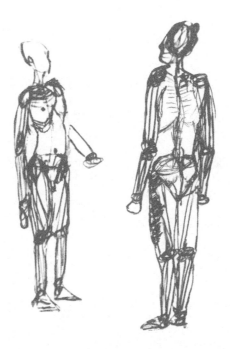

FOR MY BEAUTIFUL DAUGHTERS, Ayala and Sophie, who always inspired me to be the best version of myself, as a mother, to guide them as they take each step forward in their lives.

Editing, illustration & layout by Anna Foley Simmons ~ AnnaFoleySimmons.com

Opening three sketches by Victoria Jahkeline Salomon

Cover by Bill Wallsgrove ~ Brandad.co.uk

ISBN 9781739533700 – first edition 2023

# Acknowledgements

YANUSHKA BAGIOLO is the best teaching partner I could ask for. She started out as admin support, but once **Get Into Your Body** began to relieve her pain, her passion for practice was so profound she became the first person to sign up to train with me as an accredited **Ixchel** practitioner.

Nush's insight and enthusiasm inspire students daily on our live Zoom courses and, when I see her in action, I have no doubt this methodology will spread across the world to impact millions, even after I'm gone. Thank you to Yanushka and my six founding **Ixchel** practitioners-in-training who are helping to bring our vision to life:

Audri Schaay
Henry Tang
Keren Morris
Manuela Mazzoli
Wendy Cheverton
Yanushka Bagiolo

I'd also like to thank the delightful Anna Foley Simmons who worked for six months to edit and illustrate this manuscript, design the book's layout and launch it into bookshops and Amazon. Bill Wallsgrove of Brandad created the beautiful cover and was a pleasure to work with.

Most of all, I'd like to thank my teachers. In 2010, Meghan Mari and Rachel Fairweather of The Jing Institute in Brighton gave me the tremendous opportunity of a scholarship that supported me to take the BTEC training that was foundational to all I've learned since.

It was through Jing that I met my mentors, Gary Ward and Chris Sritharan, the extraordinary bodywork practitioners who taught me everything I know about physical alignment. Gary's seminal book **What the Foot?** and course **Anatomy in Motion** are definitive guides to physiotherapy from a bones and joints perspective. Without their teachings, **The Ixchel System**, with its focus on both physical and emotional alignment, may never have come into being. Working with these pioneers was a changing point in my life and I'm forever grateful to them.

# Contents

# INTRODUCTIONS

# BONUS:

# Your Free Video Course

---

WHY DO PEOPLE LOVE **The Ixchel System**? What's our story? How does this methodology have such a profound effect?

If you're the sort of person who loves to deep-dive into FAQ, then scan the above QR code (with your phone's camera app) or visit:

IxchelTherapies.co.uk/workbooklevel1

There you'll find a short video course with all the background and FAQ you could wish for.

Meet some of the new **Ixchel** practitioners I'm training, get extra tips on practice – and we'll keep this area continually updated with fresh material.

Some people listen to the bonus course like an audiobook (while they get on with other tasks about the house). Others sit down, with pen and paper for notetaking, and binge the videos all in one sitting. It's up to you!

This bonus video course is totally free and a great place to send friends and family who are curious about new methods for preventing and resolving pain and disease – or simply unlocking deeper states of wellness.

There's plenty of information on how to join the **Ixchel** community and book your free assessment with a trained practitioner.

Anything else you want to see there? We're always hungry to improve, so use the contact form on the website to let us know!

# Welcome!

CONGRATULATIONS on making this investment in your wellbeing.

I'm so glad you're here. 🕊

My mission is to relieve mental and physical pain by spreading awareness of these powerful practices. However, I couldn't do it if people like you weren't willing to make a commitment to transform themselves. So thank you for committing to change, and placing trust in me. It means everything.

This workbook is a practical tool. It's designed to help you make the most of the **Get Into Your Body** experience. You can use the course to access instructions for each practice. Then use the workbook to track progress, journal reflections, and deepen awareness of your body's capacity.

### So How Does Get Into Your Body Work?

Well, like you, I get stuck in body patterns that cause me pain. Sometimes it's due to repetitive strain like being hunched over a computer. Other times, it's due to emotional stress like the burden of trauma that leaves my body tensed up, in a defensive pose.

Whatever the cause, before I developed **Ixchel**, my body would get locked into this narrow range of movement which caused me all kinds of problems:

» Stressed joints
» Physical pain
» Auto-immune disease

It even locked my mental state into a narrow range of emotional patterns. I was trapped in the headspace of trauma for years.

This is the kind of crisis I see in my clients daily. It limits their full expression of potential as human beings, but it doesn't have to! **Get Into Your Body** is a gentle way to remind our system of the full range of motion that's available. As we work through these practices, it's important to understand what we're doing:

Joint by joint, muscle by muscle, we're exploring what our body is capable of.

We're learning how each of our bones is designed to move in 3D space.

We're discovering how each set of joints can align to support the structures above and below it.

We're bringing awareness into a system which may have been running on broken autopilot for as long as we can remember.

And we don't even need to fix anything! Rather, we simply bring attention to areas where our motion's restricted. We explore what movement is possible, and allow our body's magnificent autopilot system to self-correct.

In my experience, when people commit to this process, they often release decades of physical pain.

Chronic disease can clear up as body alignment relieves pressure on internal systems.

Even longstanding emotional burdens can be let go. How?

Because people release the physical restrictions that held their mental reactivity in place.

Bessel van der Kolk MD is a brilliant author to read if you want to go deeper on this topic. He describes neuroscience that supports a physical approach to mental healing. He teaches how the body 'keeps the score' of emotional trauma through patterns of misalignment and stress hormones run amok.

However, **Get Into Your Body** shows us how to wipe the scoreboard clean when it comes to embodied trauma. It shows us how to play a different game.

The key to success, in this new game, is to work with bones and joints, instead of merely muscles – and that helps us get to the source of the problem. As my mentor Gary Ward loves to say, 'Joints act; muscles react.'

Imagine a door; it only opens and shuts easily when the hinges work. Your body is no different, except that you have hundreds of hinges!

With **The Ixchel System** (of which **Get Into Your Body** is the foundational training) we continually bring attention to those all-important hinges, the bones at the joints. By focusing here, you can better observe the subtle response in your muscles when joint position changes. By attending to the hinge, we fix the door.

Pairs of muscles that work together, such as hamstrings and quads, are called agonists and antagonists. They attach to joints in the same area of the body via tendons. For example, the hamstrings and quads attach at your pelvis, knee and lower leg. If the structures they connect to can align and flow correctly in 3D, muscle movement becomes optimal and easy. Failing this, muscles get stuck or overstretched – and no amount of massage or yoga can solve the underlying misalignment problem!

With **Ixchel**, that game has changed. We're not interested in intense stretching or contraction of muscles. Those are secondary to our aim. Rather, we're looking to initiate perfect alignment that engages the joints in 3D. This then switches muscles on or off almost effortlessly so the body shifts into a state of power and freedom of movement.

With right alignment dialed in, beautiful natural boundaries arise through every range of motion, which is experienced as ease, connection, stability and safety. It feels engaged and like the body is thanking you from the core of its bones for finally understanding the crucial mechanisms that lie within. It is available to each and every one of us to support and align this gift that is the vehicle we spend our whole lives living within!

### How to Get Results with This Course

To make the most of **Get Into Your Body**, the best thing you can do is cultivate a sense of patient attention and curiosity around each part of the body we explore.

By attending to subtle changes in movement, you allow your body's autopilot to recognise where it may have gone astray.

For example, perhaps you've been clenching your shoulder unconsciously for 20 years: Only by gently showing your body it can unclench and find support from the muscles below through subtle joint realignment, can you finally provide your system the information it needs to self-correct.

This workbook will help you do that.

### Use the Power of Reflection

If your body is going to re-map itself, create integrity, and expand your capacity for movement, then first it makes sense to map the limited movement available to you right now.

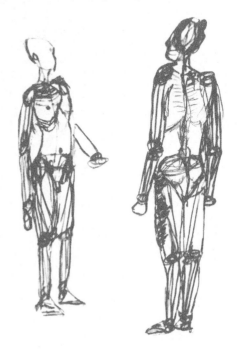

As you're going through this course, use the space provided in the workbook to make notes on the way your body feels.

Use Chris Sritharan's Ten Considerations at the back of this book to explore where your body's at right now.

Do some movements feel restricted?

Does full motion need to be restored?

Any limitation you discover is something to be celebrated. It means you've found a pattern of physical misalignment which can be brought into awareness and worked with.

That is the purpose of the practice!

**Use the Power of Pacing**

'How many reps should I do?'

This is the question everyone asks. The truth of the answer is, 'It depends.'

One simple rule of thumb is to move slowly in and out of each movement five times.

However, the big-picture answer is, 'We want you to build these movements into your daily life. So, while you're standing in the queue, while you're sitting at your desk, can you gently move each body part in multiple planes of motion?'

The fact is, this isn't a CrossFit class; it's not a competition with yourself over how many reps you can smash. Rather, it's an intuitive process where slow, gentle, feel-good movements will help your nervous system integrate the practice.

It's better to do one slow movement, with awareness and alignment, rather than many rushed repetitions where the integrity of the movement is lost.

To stay aware, pay attention to the sensation of the movement. To stay aligned, don't make the common error of presuming you've got the movement right. Rather, watch yourself in the mirror and refer to the course videos to be sure your movement's a match.

Even if you get a practice right once, it's so easy to fall back into old habits, so keep gently checking your alignment till it becomes second nature.

If you're taking the **Get Into Your Body** course, you'll be working with a new body part each week. A good approach is twofold:

» Explore the new movement by yourself (making notes in this workbook)
» Practice with feedback from an **Ixchel** practitioner (if you're part of a live session)

» In addition, as part of daily life, you could run through the previous movements you've learned so far (making sure each new practice is built on aligned foundations – so you don't become the Leaning Tower of Pisa!)

Don't beat yourself up if you can't manage all this weekly. Some students take 7 weeks to complete Level 1, but others take 7 months and still get excellent results.

Your pace will depend on how much pain, energy and free time you have. The crucial thing is to focus on building alignment, safety and connection.

Each movement builds upon the supportive base of alignment beneath – like a cherry placed

atop an ice-cream sundae. Just doing one rep of one practice correctly gives far more benefit than a thousand reps with a body misaligned.

If you have any concerns, I suggest you have one of our qualified practitioners assess your movement to check you're not doing the right thing wrongly.

### Use the Power of Writing

Have a flip through this workbook now. You'll see brief reminders of each practice with simple sketches to refresh your memory. You can even scan the QR codes to link back to the course video (be sure to log in first). To scan a QR code, simply open the camera app on your smartphone and point it at the gray square on any practice page.

We've allowed wide margins to make room for your notes and, after each practice, there is space to journal your reflections. This is where the real work happens!

To track your progress, why not note your pain level on a scale of 1 to 10? Jot down any lack of mobility. You could also date your notes to track progress over time.

At each bullet list, you'll find questions to guide self-assessment. We encourage you to answer these with words and doodles – label, annotate, record sensations to remind yourself of areas you want to work on.

Check your body position in the mirror or measure it against an imaginary clock face. Can you use our illustrations as inspiration to sketch the contours of your alignment?

Drawing, much like writing, is a deeper way of thinking and can help you reflect on this process and allow your unconscious mind to integrate everything you learn.

### Use the Power of Attention

As in life, so with Get Into Your Body: the more awareness you can bring to your capacities and limitations, the easier it will be to progress.

This is a beautiful and challenging process where you will light up each part of your body with self-knowledge. It's a chance for old, fractured patterns of behaviour to integrate into a wholesome, new understanding of what's possible for you and your body.

Well done for making this commitment to elevate your health and wellbeing. Now, all you need do is be patient with yourself as you move through the practices.

Stay attentive, keep being curious and most of all, enjoy the ride!

Victoria Salomon

PS. At the back of this workbook is a list of all 48 practices. Refer to this for a quick refresher of the whole course. If you'd like, cut that page out, so you can pin it on the fridge for ease of review.

Before you start the workbook, I recommend you flip back to the appendix at the end. You'll see tables to track alignment, 10 considerations to guide reflection, and diagrams to inspire your sketches. Your sketches don't need to be fine art – more like kids' drawings with pain and pressure areas coloured in. Have fun with it!

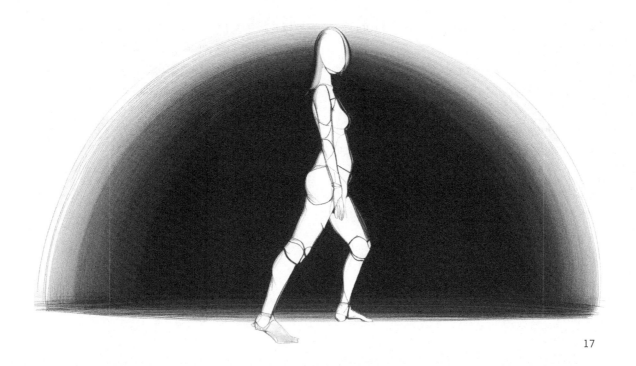

# The Story of Your Body

BEFORE YOU BEGIN to explore these life changing practices, take some time to reflect on your body's journey so far.

» What brought you to the **Get Into Your Body** course?
» Do you have a history of injury or chronic pain?
» Do you have emotional pain that impacts your body due to past experiences?

We've provided three pages for you to journal your thoughts but, if you're a writing enthusiast, you may wish to purchase a beautiful notebook and allow yourself to dive deeper into these reflections. The more awareness you can bring to your body's needs, the richer your experience will be.

Also, if you realise that emotional pain and trauma are areas you want to explore more deeply, you might be interested in **The Ixchel System DNA Pain Relief** course, which is wholly focused on trauma healing.

When you're writing the story of your body, include accidents, emotional traumas, repetitive strain injuries, postural issues, anything at all that may have impacted your body over time.

» How was it in the past? How is it now? And what do you hope to gain from **Get Into Your Body**? Review your past and set intentions for the future.

# ✎ THE STORY OF MY BODY

_____

_____

_____

_____

_____

_____

_____

_____

_____

_____

_____

_____

_____

_____

_____

_____

_____

_____

## ✎ THE STORY OF MY BODY

## ✏ THE STORY OF MY BODY

# The Pain Scale

AS YOU GO THROUGH these practices, rate your discomfort on a scale of 1 to 10.

This could be emotional pain triggered by a movement that releases old memories. It could be frustration over your level of body knowledge. It could be depression, confusion, even that creeping feeling of self-doubt that says, 'This isn't for me.'

In terms of physical discomfort, you might feel lack of mobility, stiffness or pain caused by using your body in a new way. The most important thing to remember is this:

**If any pain goes above a 7 (8 to 10), that means STOP.** There's no benefit from gritting your teeth and powering through.

However, pain that is 7 and below is your body's way of speaking to you. It's crucial information that can guide us.

If we listen to the messages our body is sending (between levels 1 and 7) we bring light to the darkness of unconscious habits. We begin to understand the causes of our discomfort and reduce the onset of level 8 pain and above.

If you feel overwhelmed, ground yourself in the foot tripod, (a method you'll learn in Module 1). This restores feelings of safety.

Connect. Breathe. Let go of the urge to suppress. Reflect on what you're doing and how. Give yourself permission to feel that pain. What is it trying to tell you?

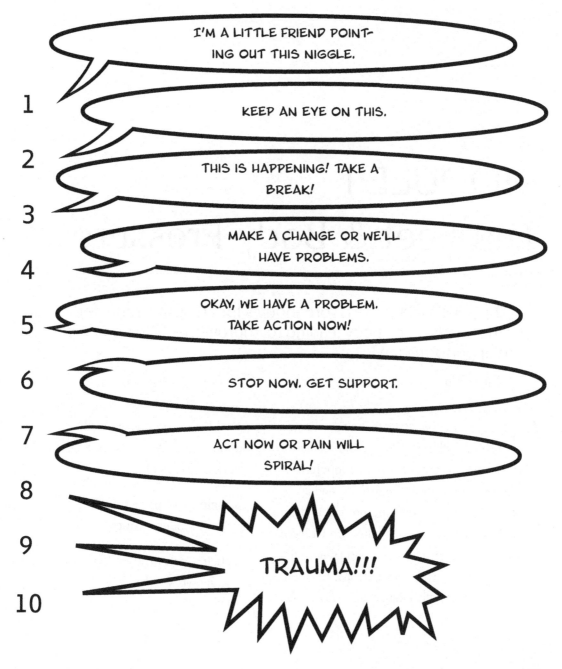

# MODULE 1
# The Feet & Body Pressure

'The smallest change in somebody's foot reaps unexpected rewards in other areas of the body leading to improvements in people's pain and their performance.'

~ Gary Ward

GET READY TO CONNECT with the miracle mechanics of the 26 bones and 33 joints of your feet. Good foot mechanics support your centre of mass, mobilise your body, and allow optimal engagement with the ground and up through the body. In this module, you'll learn how to orient in the clock face and create a flat and arched foot, which are essential to orient and stabilise every other joint in the body above.

You'll begin to understand the importance of good boundaries in your range of motion for effortless movement.

**Can help solve:** plantar fasciitis; sprains, strains and breaks; bunions; foot pain.

**Can help create:** a grounded feeling of standing on your own two feet.

# Practice 1

## STANDING IN THE CLOCK FACE

**W**ITH EYES FOCUSED on the horizon and feet hip-width apart, your second toes point towards 12 o'clock with knees fully extended above your heels (no leaning forward or back).

» Can you feel your body weight going down through your feet?

» Can you see in a long mirror that your body is aligned and not leaning?

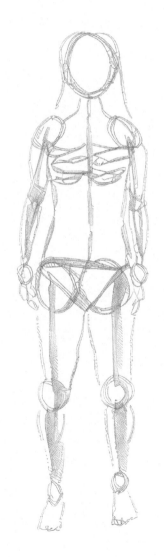

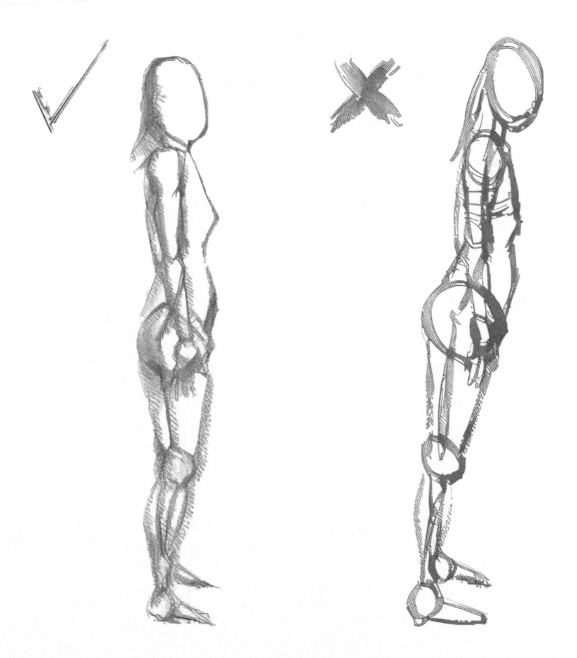

Sketch ✍

➤ Small movements lead to big shifts in alignment ✦

JOURNAL

# Practice 2
# THE FOOT TRIPOD

STANDING ALIGNED in the clock face, you feel into your foot tripod, one foot at a time.

» Can you feel the three points of contact?
» Is it easy to keep all three points evenly connected with the ground?
» Does the tripod feel more connected to the ground in one foot compared to the other?
» If you insert a wedge or piece of cloth, what difference does it make?
» Where do you need to insert the wedge or cloth in order to feel connected?
» How does the rest of your body feel different with the wedge or cloth inserted?

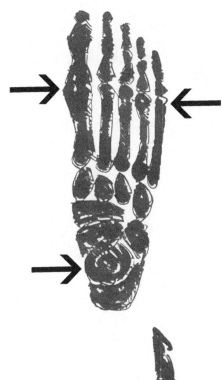

SKETCH ⮌

Small movements lead to big shifts in alignment ⤴

✏️ JOURNAL

# Practice 3

## FOOT PRESSURE & PRONATION

YOU STAND WITH FEET hip-width apart and second toes facing 12 o'clock. Keeping foot tripods grounded you turn your body towards 3 o'clock.

» How far can you go without either foot losing contact with the ground?

» Can you notice how your left foot is flattening into the ground (pronation)?

» How far can your turn towards 3 o'clock before your left foot fifth met wants to lose contact with the ground?

Staying aligned and grounded you now turn your body towards 9 o'clock.

» How far can you go without either foot losing contact with the ground?

» Can you notice how your right foot is flattening into the ground (pronation)?

» How far can your turn towards 9 o'clock be-

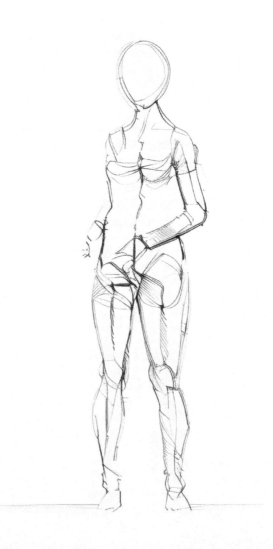

fore your right foot fifth met wants to lose contact with the ground?

You let your pronating foot soften and spread as you move slowly from 12 to 3 or 9 o'clock and let your body start to familiarise the sensation of the spreading foot.

» As you rotate towards 3 o'clock, can you feel your foot pressure move toward the inside of your left foot?

» As you rotate towards 9 o'clock, can you feel your foot pressure move toward the inside of your right foot?

» Are you driving from the front of the ankle (the talus, 'driver of the bus' shown by the arrow)? Or is your upper body pulling you around?

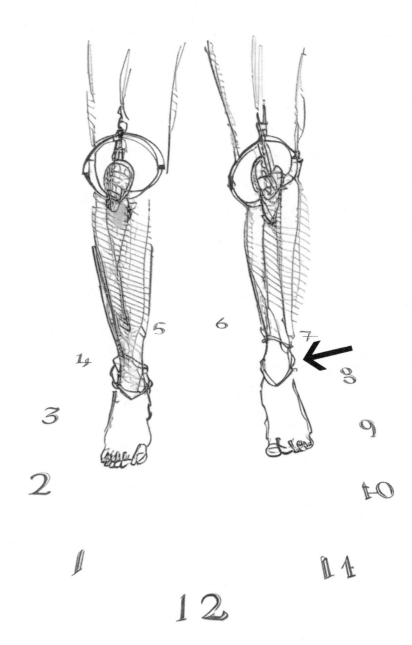

## SKETCH ✍

➤ Small movements lead to big shifts in alignment ✎

## ✎ JOURNAL

_____

_____

_____

_____

_____

_____

_____

_____

_____

_____

_____

_____

_____

_____

_____

_____

_____

_____

_____

_____

# Practice 4

# FOOT PRESSURE & SUPINATION

YOU STAND WITH FEET hip-width apart and second toes facing 12 o'clock. Keeping foot tripods grounded you turn your body towards 3 o'clock. How far can you go without either foot losing contact with the ground?

» Can you notice how your right foot arch is rising with the turn (supination)?
» How far can you turn towards 3 o'clock before your left foot fifth met wants to lose contact with the ground?

Staying aligned and grounded you now turn your body towards 9 o'clock.

» How far can you go without either foot losing contact with the ground?
» Can you notice how your left foot arch is rising with the turn (supination)?

» How far can you turn towards 9 o'clock before your right foot fifth met wants to lose contact with the ground?

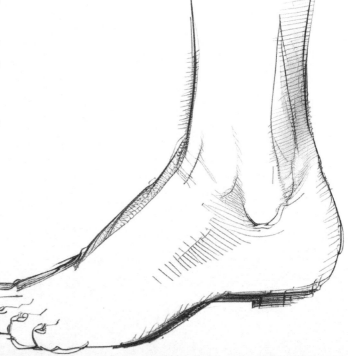

You let your supinating foot engage all its bones and muscles as
you move slowly from 12 to 3 or
9 o'clock and let your body start
to familiarise the sensation of the
supported foot.

» As you rotate towards 3
o'clock, can you feel your foot
pressure move toward the
outside of the right foot?

» As you rotate towards 9
o'clock, can you feel your foot
pressure move toward the
outside of the left foot?

Sketch ✍

➤➤ Small movements lead to big shifts in alignment ✒

✏️ JOURNAL

# Practice 5

# WEIGHT SINKING THROUGH LEGS & FEET

STANDING ALIGNED in the clock face, you feel into your foot tripod, one foot at a time.

» Can you feel a difference in pressure in one foot compared to the other?

» Feeling into one foot at a time, can you tell if there is more pressure on the front or back of the foot, on the inside or outside of the foot?

Moving from your ankles, you turn your body towards 3 o'clock.

» How far can you go before your pelvis naturally stops and before your right first met wants to lift off the ground?

Now you move your weight into your left leg without your pelvis turning sideways towards 9 o'clock.

With both feet on the floor facing 12 o'clock, and the weight in the left leg, you rotate from the ankles towards 3 o'clock.

» How far you can go around the clock face before first met on the right foot wants to lift off the ground?

» Can you feel more mobility and flexibility in your movement?

You return to 12 o'clock.

Now you repeat the process with all your weight going down your right leg, and rotating towards 3 o'clock.

» Can you feel a restriction in the movement?

Repeat the above, but moving towards 9 o'clock, first with your weight in both legs, then in the right leg, and finally in the left leg.

» Are you becoming aware of where the weight is distributed through your body and how it affects **your movement?**

» When you experiment with **wedges, what** difference does it **make?**

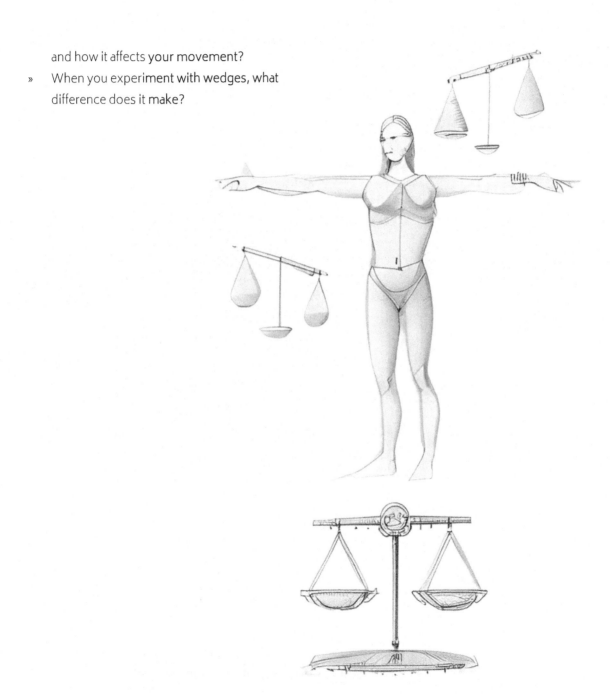

## SKETCH ✍

➤ Small movements lead to big shifts in alignment ✎

✎ JOURNAL

# Practice 6

## SUSPENSION ~ FRONT LEG FLEXING FORWARD

Y OU KEEP YOUR EYES on the horizon and take a normal step forward, as if you're walking. The second toe of your front foot points to 12 o'clock. You sit into your front leg, causing your knee to bend (flexion).

You keep your rib cage and head above your pelvis and avoid leaning forwards over the front leg. You keep your knee above the corridor of your foot, avoiding it going over the inside or outside edge. You keep all three points of the tripod on the ground.

» As you move in and out of this position, do you notice how your body weight moves through your front foot?

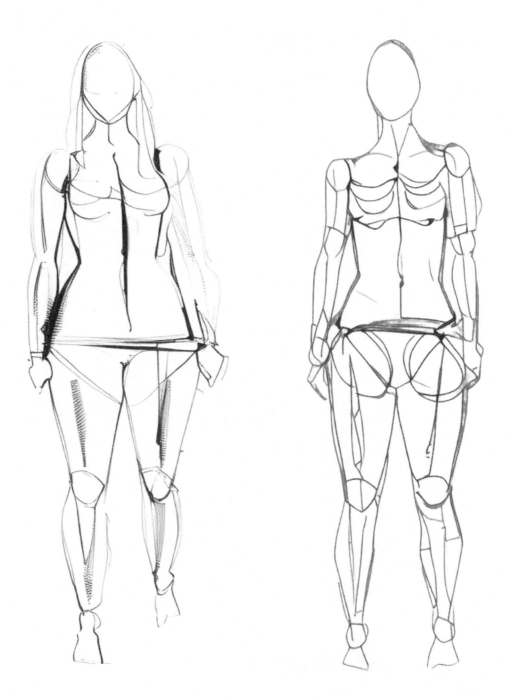

## Sketch ✍

➤ Small movements lead to big shifts in alignment ✒

## ✎ JOURNAL

# Practice 7

# PROPULSION ~ BACK LEG TO PUSH THE PELVIS FORWARD

YOU KEEP YOUR EYES on the horizon and take a normal step forward with your right leg as if you're walking. You feel your back foot (left) against the ground, then push up from the ball of your foot, so that you lift your heel off the ground.

You keep the knee of your back leg fully extended and straight. You practice lifting up and down from your back foot so that it pushes your body forward through the momentum of the ball of your foot. As the heel lifts, it pushes the body forwards.

As your left heel fully comes off the ground, you keep first and fifth met facing 12 o'clock and rotate your left hip, knee and ankle away from your body (towards 9 o'clock).

You keep your pelvis facing forwards towards 12 o'clock so that your hip joint rotates, rather than your whole body turning towards 9 o'clock.

» Can you feel a spiraling sensation going through the muscles of your back leg?

Now you practice **this** movement in time with suspension (practice 6). The heel comes off the ground as you bend and sink into your front leg.

SKETCH

➻ Small movements lead to big shifts in alignment ✒

# MODULE 2
# The Pelvis & Hip Alignment

'Physical self-awareness is the first step in releasing the tyranny of the past.'

~ Bessel van der Kolk

Now, AS YOU GET FAMILIAR with the pelvis, exploring its range of movement, you'll almost become your own osteopath. By learning to assess the boundaries of movement in your own joints, you can avoid creating pain, or potentially relieve pain, through understanding which movements compress or overstrain your hips and back. Also, since the pelvis is the seat of the nervous system, generating stability here creates support for your upper body and all the systems it contains.

**Can help solve:** back pain; hip pain.

**Can help create:** a feeling of finally being supported, physically and emotionally.

# Sagittal Plane

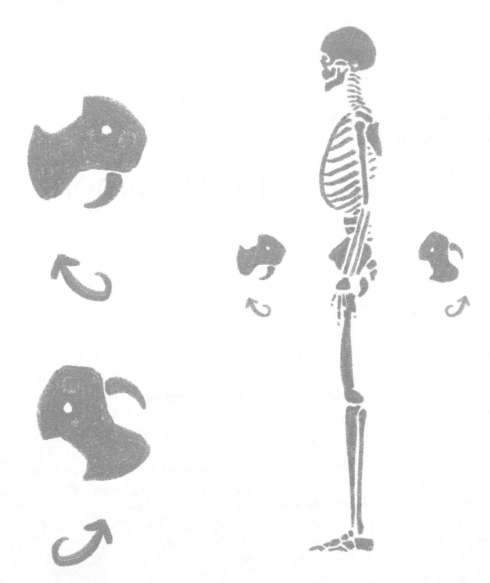

# Frontal Plane        Transverse Plane

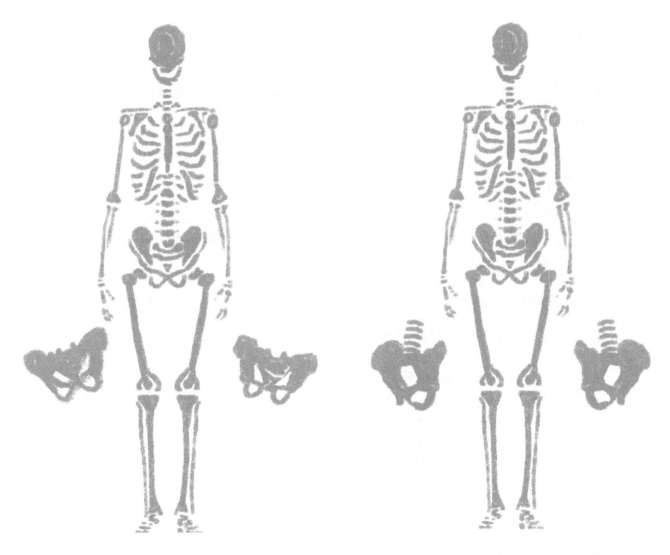

# Practice 8

# CONNECTING WITH MOVEMENTS OF THE PELVIS

LYING DOWN, you allow your pelvis to sink into the ground with legs bent, feet flat, and heels as close to your buttocks as possible.

» As you feel the weight of your pelvis sinking into the ground, do you notice whether you feel the same amount of pressure going through the left and right side of your buttocks into the ground?

You rock your pelvis up and down.

» How does this feel in your lower back?
» How does it feel in your thighs?
» What part of your body are you using to rock your pelvis?
» Are you able to simply rock the bony pelvic bowl from your hips or are your legs or lower back doing the movement instead?

You try to do a very small rocking movement of the pelvis but feel it coming from your hip joints (top of the middle of your thighs).

» Does this seem strange and difficult at first?
» Can you begin to feel the difference between the sensation of engaging joints compared with the sensation of contracting and releasing muscles?
» What plane of movement is this?

SKETCH ✒

➤ Small movements lead to big shifts in alignment ✒

JOURNAL

# Practice 9

# STANDING WITH YOUR PELVIS AGAINST THE WALL

YOU STAND AGAINST A WALL and feel the back of your pelvis pushing into it.

» Does your alignment allow your head to rest against the wall, with chin pointing down to the ground? Or does your chin have to point forward, for your skull to tip back and touch the wall?

If your chin points forward, you flex your knees and move feet further away from the wall to allow your legs to bend until you are lower and your head is nearer the wall.

You rock your pelvis backwards and forwards, so the arch in your lower back gets bigger, and then flattens out against the wall.

» Is this an easy movement, or does part of your body, legs or lower back find it difficult?

If this is difficult, you make it into a smaller movement that comes from the hip joints.

## SKETCH ✍

➤ Small movements lead to big shifts in alignment ✒

✎ JOURNAL

# Practice 10

# ANTERIOR & POSTERIOR PELVIC TILT IN SAGITTAL PLANE

YOU STAND WITH FEET hip-width apart and second toes facing 12 o'clock.

» Is your belly button also facing 12 o'clock?

You send your pelvis back (anterior pelvic tilt) so that, if it was a bowl of water, it would tip forward, spilling liquid on your toes. It feels like you're sticking your bottom out behind you.

» Is it easy to move your pelvis back into the wall or does it immediately feel bunched up

in your lower back?

If it feels immediately bunched up, your natural resting position may be anterior pelvic tilt. If this is the case, tuck your bottom under, so your coccyx (small bone at the end of your spine) tucks underneath and the arch of your lower back flattens a little.

» In your feet, where do you naturally feel the weight going down?

» When you anteriorly tilt your pelvis, is your

weight more on the inside of your feet or the outside of your feet?

» When you tuck your bottom under (posterior pelvic tilt) is your weight more on the inside of your feet or the outside of your feet?

You practice moving between these two movements.

» When you anterior pelvic tilt, does the weight sink more into the front of your feet or the back of your feet?

» When you posterior pelvic tilt, does your weight move into the front of your feet, or back of your feet?

» With an anterior tilt, when your body rotates towards 3 o'clock notice what happens in your feet?

» With an anterior tilt, when your body rotates towards 9 o'clock, what happens in your feet?

» Can you isolate and move your pelvis on its own? Or is it your knees, legs, or upper body that are pulling or pushing your pelvis backward and forwards, without actually engaging the biomechanical movement of the pelvis itself?

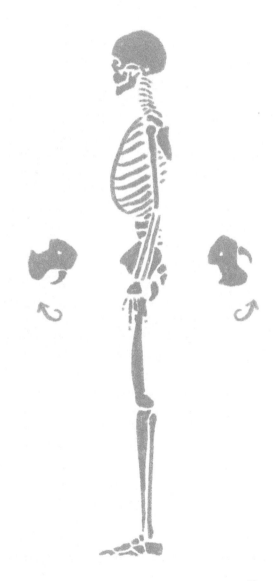

## SKETCH ✑

➤ Small movements lead to big shifts in alignment ✐

## ✎ JOURNAL

# Practice 11

# HIKED HIPS IN FRONTAL PLANE

YOU STAND WITH FEET and second toes facing 12 o'clock. Your knees are positioned above your heels, knees fully extended, hips above knees.

With your pelvis in a fairly neutral position in sagittal plane (from the side-view), you bend your right leg. Your left leg keeps its knee fully extended.

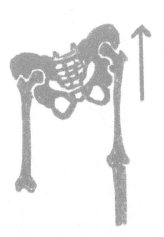

» Where is your weight sinking down through your legs and your feet?
» Do you feel more weight passing through your left leg, which is straight, or your right leg, which is bent?

If you feel a lot of body weight sinking down the right bent leg, you try gently hiking your pelvis up more on the left side.

You gently bring most of your body weight into your left leg. You have the intention of bringing your body weight into your straight left leg, without sending your pelvis left.

» Does your upper body feels nicely supported with most of your weight distributed through the left straight leg?

Now you straighten the right leg, bending the left leg.

» Do you naturally find your body collapses its weight down through the left bent leg? Or is your weight easily sent down through your right, straight leg?

You should be able to pick the bent leg foot off

the floor. You keep the heel of the bent leg firmly on the floor, even though the leg is bent.

You alternate the above movement between legs aiming for flow of motion.

» When you use gravity and move most of your upper body weight into the straight leg and out of the bent leg, can you sense your pelvis is moving up and down in the frontal plane, like a see-saw?

» Is the movement uncomfortable at any point?

Rather than move into pain, if anything is uncomfortable, you make your movement smaller, find the edge between comfort and discomfort, and move within that range.

If uncomfortable, you can try to shift your pelvis into more of a posterior or anterior tilt.

» How does this shift affect the sensation in your lower back?

» How does it affect the feeling of support from your feet and legs going up into your pelvis?

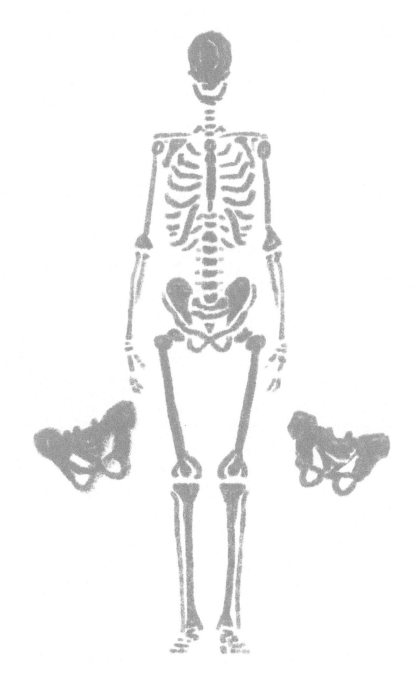

SKETCH ✍

➤ Small movements lead to big shifts in alignment ✦

✏ JOURNAL

# Practice 12

# ROTATING THE PELVIS IN TRANSVERSE PLANE

YOUR FEET, SECOND TOES AND PELVIS face 12 o'clock and your knees are locked above your feet.

Your knees are still and facing forwards. Your rib cage and head face forwards. You rotate your pelvis towards 3 o'clock. It can be quite a small movement.

» Do your knees or upper body want to move with your pelvis? Or are you able to move your pelvis without them?

You bring your pelvis towards 9 o'clock.

» Can you move your pelvis on its own? Or do your knees, rib cage, or even your head, want to move with your pelvis?

You repeat the movement a few times.

» Are you sending the movement from the front or back of your pelvis?
» Which side is easier, and which side is hard-er to move?
» What happens in your feet? Are the tripods of the right and left feet each easily staying on the ground when you go in both direc-tions?

You play with shifting weight onto the right leg and rotating towards 9 o'clock. Then you shift weight onto the left leg and rotate towards 9 o'clock.

Next, you play with shifting weight onto the left leg and rotating towards 3 o'clock. Then you shift weight onto the right leg and rotate towards 3 o'clock.

» When you focus on your feet, how do they feel when you move in each direction?
» Do these movements feel confusing at first?
» Are you able to separate out pelvic rotation in transverse plane (view from above) from the rotation of rib cage or skull?

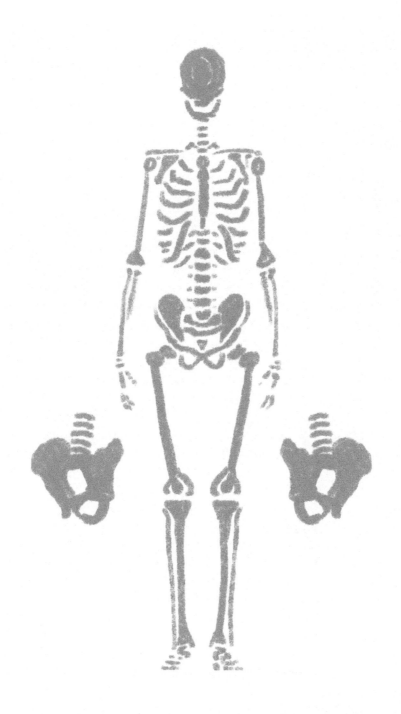

## SKETCH

Small movements lead to big shifts in alignment

✏️ JOURNAL

# Practice 13

# ONE LEG FORWARD ~ THE PELVIS IN SAGITTAL PLANE

YOU TAKE A NORMAL STEP forward with your right leg. Both feet face 12 o'clock with feet hip-width apart.

You keep your head and rib cage above your pelvis and sit into your right leg. Letting your right knee flex, move it from above the outside of the heel through the corridor of the foot towards the second toe.

» As you flex the knee and move forward, what is happening with your pelvis? Can you feel any anterior or posterior tilt movement? (You're looking for anterior tilt, where the coccyx is sent back).

» What's happening with your spine and pelvis as you sink forward into the front leg?

» Can you feel your lower back extending and arching as you flex slowly into the knee?

» Can you feel if your spine is extending, or does it simply feel stiff, rigid and stuck?

» Can you feel your spine and pelvis connection?

You move back to neutral and straighten both legs. Your spine should soften with the arch, flattening a little.

Next you bring the left leg forward, and sit into it, flexing the knee through the corridor of the foot. You keep your head and rib cage above your pelvis.

» Can you feel your lower back arching (extending) slightly?

» As you straighten the leg, can you feel the arch of your back flattening a little?

» What's happening with your pelvis? Is your pelvis tilting as if your bottom is sticking out slightly behind you? Or does your pelvis feel stuck as you flex the left knee and sit into your left foot?

» Overall, when you sit into your front legs

do you feel your lower back arching more with an anterior tilt, and the coccyx pointing backward?

»   Does it feel the same or different with the left and right legs?

You begin to become aware of your thigh bones (femurs) and how the top end is your hip and the bottom end is your knee.

»   Can you feel the connection of your thigh bone with your lower leg and also your pelvis?

You focus on putting this suspension movement into action in a fluid motion.

SKETCH

»→ Small movements lead to big shifts in alignment ✦

✎ JOURNAL

# Practice 14

# PROPULSION ~ BACK LEG TO PUSH THE PELVIS FORWARD

YOU TAKE THE RIGHT LEG back and bend the front (left) leg. You allow the heel of the back foot to come off the ground.

You have a sense of the ball of the back leg foot pushing you forward.

Keeping the first and fifth met of your right foot on the ground, you push forward from the back leg.

You rotate the hip, knee and talus bone in the foot of your back leg away from the body, but keep your second toe facing 12 o'clock.

You allow the front-leg-side of the pelvis to rise. As you reach the end of the rotation of the back leg that side of the pelvis will be lower.

» Can you finish the journey, getting as far as you can, without the first and fifth met of the back foot leaving the ground?

» If not, can you use a wedge or some cloth to support the fifth met and keep the back foot facing 12 o'clock?

If you feel the glute muscles in the buttocks tighten and a feeling of your pelvis tucking under on the back-leg side, you are moving into the correct response for a posterior tilt.

You move slowly in and out of propulsion, with the back foot gently but buoyantly pushing the whole body forward. Your back hip and leg rotate away from the body while keeping first and fifth met on the ground.

As you do this, you feel the pelvis on the back leg side squeezing or tucking under in sagittal plane (seen from side view), and sinking down sideways in the frontal plane (seen from front view). You're looking for the pelvis to naturally drop back and down.

» As you play with spiraling the back-leg muscles into propulsion, and keeping the correct movement of your pelvis tucking under, does the new movement feel strange?

» Can you sense how a lack of mobility may feel more normal for you and may have been the source of stiffness or pain?

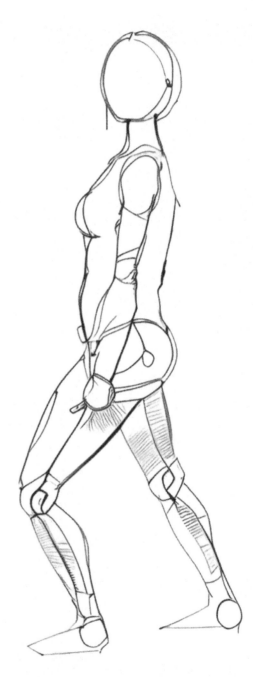

## SKETCH

Small movements lead to big shifts in alignment

## 🖉 JOURNAL

# Practice 15

# HIKED HIP MOVING FORWARD IN FRONTAL PLANE

YOU FLEX YOUR LEFT KNEE, moving it forward and backwards, with the left knee bending into suspension. Suspension is the phase of gait when the front leg takes the weight of your body. You have a sense of the knee end of your left thigh bone moving slightly inwards in the direction of 1 o'clock.

As you move forwards towards one 1 o'clock, you keep your pelvis following your knee, but not rotating too far (going more forward than sideways).

» Can you sense your left hip rising slightly?

You take your right arm upwards. As you flex your left knee, you start to see how your pelvis moves as you flex your knee.

You repeat this with the right foot. As you flex forward, flexing the knee, your right hip should rise and hike.

As you move back to have both feet flat on the floor, your pelvis levels. As you flex your knee forward, your front leg hip rises as the back leg hip sinks. You feel into this.

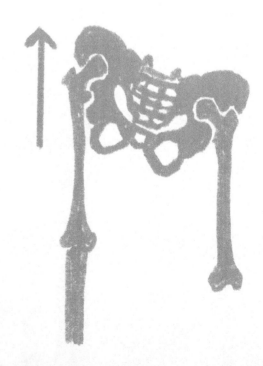

» Can you feel that happening or does it feel stuck?
» As you move forward, can you feel the weight moving from the back of the heel to the front of the foot?
» How does it feel in your knee in that movement?
» How does it feel in the front leg?

You make the movement very slow and feel the movement between the hip and the pelvis, keeping an eye on the foot tripod.

Overall can you sense the way your hip joint is designed to rise on the front leg side of your pelvis? Can you sense how this is also the side of your pelvis that is taking the weight of your body, while your back leg propels you forward and lifts off the ground as the leg swings forward?

You keep thinking, 'This is what my body does: It walks.'

## SKETCH ✍

➤ Small movements lead to big shifts in alignment ✒

✏️ JOURNAL

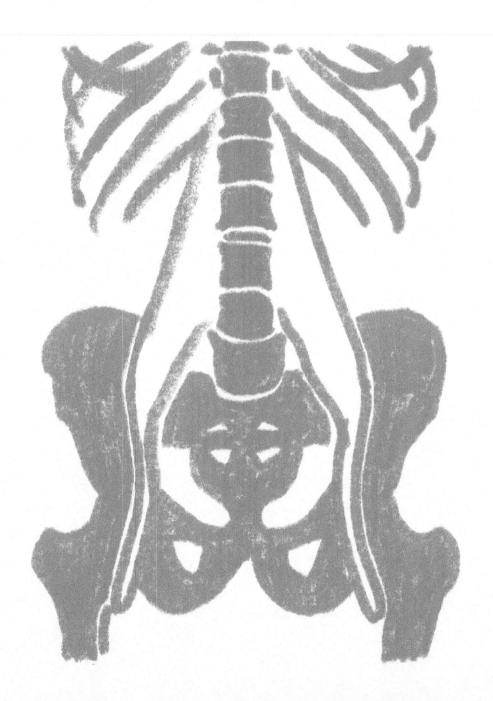

# MODULE 3
# Spinal Alignment

'The body has been designed to renew itself through continuous self-correction. These same principles also apply to the healing of psyche, spirit, and soul.'

~ Peter A. Levine

WITH PELVIS STABILISED, it's time to support the spine. In this module, you'll learn to activate the psoas muscle and thereby engage the joints where the psoas attaches to your hips and the base of your rib cage.

It's an extraordinary experience to realise that suddenly, all the little vertebrae at the base of the spine are no longer being forced to support the upper body. Instead the psos switches on and, for many of our students, it creates a sense of support, release safety and protection, which they have never experienced before.

**Can help solve:** symptoms of menopause, menstrual cycle and hormonal issues; fibromyalgia; chronic fatigue syndrome; IBS; ADHD.

**Can help create:** a feeling of safety in your skin and the release of embodied trauma.

# Practice 16

# FINDING THE HIP FLEXORS

To FEEL THE MOVEMENT of your hip flexors, you sit on a firm chair with your knees at 90 degrees, hip-width apart, feet flat on the floor.

You place your fingers over the bony points at the bottom of the front of your pelvis. These are above the middle of your thigh.

You fold your spine forwards so you are looking at the floor with your fingers pushing into your groin, in between the bottom of your pelvis and your thigh.

You want to feel the bony points at the bottom of your pelvis crushing your fingers, as your pelvis folds on top of your thighs.

You repeat this two or three times so you get a clear sensation in your body of the hip flexor attachment points where the pelvis connects to the thighs on the inside

of your hips. The hip flexors look like this.

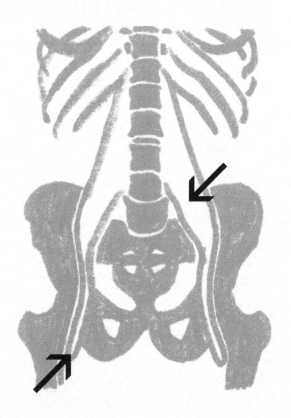

SKETCH ⮎

➤ Small movements lead to big shifts in alignment ➹

JOURNAL

# Practice 17

# ALIGNING THE SPINE ABOVE THE PELVIS

YOU SIT AS YOU WERE in the previous practice, folded forwards. You slowly unfold from the sitting position with your fingers still touching the area of your groin where the hip flexors are.

You keep your spine moving upwards and back until you feel the area around your groin fully engage.

» Do you feel as if this is pushing the front of your pelvis slightly forward?
» Do you feel the muscles in your buttocks (glutes) engage and your pelvis tuck under into a more neutral posterior tilt?
» How does your upper body feel? (You should feel upright and as though your upper body is completely supported.)

You recheck your feet and make sure they're aligned, with your second toes facing 12 o'clock. (If this is painful, then you have them as close to

12 o'clock as is comfortable.)

You practice this a few times, moving from the folded sitting position to unfolding your spine upwards and fully engaging the hip flexors so your thigh muscles and the muscles of your belly feel completely engaged.

» As you lift up your spine and rib cage, together with engaging the bottom of your hip flexors, so that your abdomen muscles engage from above and below, can you feel how your belly flattens a little?

You make sure your rib cage is directly above your pelvis and not leaning forwards.

» Can you notice that, if you do lean forwards, your eyes naturally look down towards the floor, and then you have to lift your head up and back, which contracts the back of your neck?

» Can you feel how engaged hip flexors:

» Bring your spine upright instead of leaning slightly forwards?

» Push forward from the lower hip flexor attachment point in your groin?

» Engage the muscles at the back of your pelvis (glutes)?

» Relieves pressure on your lower back and aligns your pelvis?

» Allows abdominal muscles to relax a little?

» Tones your muscles better than sit-ups?

Going forward, when you stand up, you engage the glute and hip flexor area at the end of the range as your spine aligns your upper body. This supports the front of your body, taking pressure away from the curve of your lower back and helping to create a strong foundation in the lower body to support your upper body.

SKETCH

➻ Small movements lead to big shifts in alignment ✒

✎  JOURNAL

# Practice 18

# SPINE & PELVIS IN SAGITTAL PLANE

YOU ALIGN YOUR SPINE and engage your hip flexors. Now you gently move your pelvis into anterior and posterior tilt.

» Do you notice how it's now a much smaller movement?

» How is the experience of moving into an anterior tilt when you focus on engaging your hip flexors?

» You'll feel the hip flexors soften slightly, but can you still feel the strength of the movement coming from the area around the groin?

» How is the experience of the posterior tilt? Can you feel a much smaller but stronger movement than you did in practice 10?

» Can you notice how it is no longer the lower back and lumbar curve area doing all the movement of the tilts? Instead, can you feel how the hip flexors and spine support the upper body without your centre of mass

collapsing into your lumbar vertebrae?

You revisit what you did in practice 10 with your sagittal plane pelvic tilts. However, this time you do it with your focus on having hip flexors engaged and your spine and rib cage above your pelvis, rather than collapsing, softening at the hip flexor connection or leaning forwards.

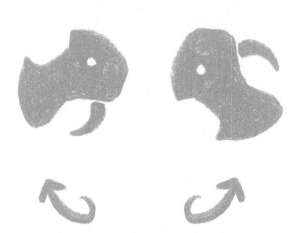

SKETCH

➤ Small movements lead to big shifts in alignment ↗

✎ JOURNAL

_____
_____
_____
_____
_____
_____
_____
_____
_____
_____
_____
_____
_____
_____
_____
_____
_____
_____
_____

# Practice 19

# ALIGNING THE SUPPORT OF HIP FLEXORS IN SUSPENSION LEG

NOW YOU REVISIT practice 6 and 13. However, this time you bring your attention to the area of your groin and the sensation of where your hip flexors attach.

You bend your front knee, keeping your spine aligned above your body, and your front leg hip flexor engaged.

You sit into your front leg, keeping your knee moving forward in the corridor of the foot in line with the second toe at 12 o'clock.

You don't let the knee go further forward than the second toe, or you'll feel the heel want to come off the ground and lose your tripod.

You keep your spine upright and supported by your hip flexor which may feel about 50% engaged in the flexed front leg.

» Can you notice that, if the knee collapses over the inside of the edge of your front foot, the groin support for your upper body collapses?

» Can you notice that, if the knee goes over the outside edge of your front foot, you feel unstable and the inside of your heel wants to leave the ground?

You repeat the above process by bringing your opposite leg forward.

» Do you notice whether it's a different experience with this leg?

» Is it easier or harder to flow through the motion and feel the hip flexor engaging?

Sᴋᴇᴛᴄʜ

⇶ Small movements lead to big shifts in alignment ↗

JOURNAL

# Practice 20

## ALIGNING THE SUPPORT OF HIP FLEXORS IN PROPULSION LEG

AGAIN YOU REVISIT practice 6 and 13, bringing your attention to your groin area and the sensation of where your hip flexors attach.

You bend your front knee, keeping your spine aligned above your body, and your front leg hip flexor engaged.

You sit into your front leg, keeping your knee moving forward in the corridor of the foot in line with the second toe at 12 o'clock.

You don't let the knee go further forward than the second toe, or you'll feel the heel want to come off the ground and lose your tripod.

> » You keep your spine upright and supported by your hip flexor which may feel about 50% engaged in the flexed front leg.
> » Can you notice that, if the knee collapses over the inside of the edge of your front foot, the groin support for your upper body collapses?
> » Can you notice that, if the knee goes over the outside edge of your front foot, you feel unstable and the inside of your heel wants to leave the ground, along with first met?

You repeat the above process by bringing your opposite leg forward.

> » Do you notice whether it's a different experience with this leg?
> » Is it easier or harder to flow through the motion and feel the hip flexor engaging?

## SKETCH ✏️

➤ Small movements lead to big shifts in alignment ✐

✏️ JOURNAL

# MODULE 4
# Connecting with the Rib Cage

'Healing depends on experiential knowledge: You can be fully in charge of your life only if you can acknowledge the reality of your body, in all its visceral dimensions.'

~ Bessel A. van der Kolk

LET'S SEE IF YOU CAN isolate the movement of your rib cage. Most people can't, at first. They move their head with their rib cage or they move their pelvis with their rib cage and very seldom do they actually move their rib cage in isolation in any plane of movement. This means muscles and blood flow are simply not functioning correctly around the heart, lungs and digestive tract, so with rib cage release, we give you the extraordinary opportunity to finally move your rib cage in isolation.

**Can help solve:** breathing issues; chest pain or tightness; pneumonia; asthma; digestive issues; post-chemo symptoms; bodily tension.

**Can help create:** a feeling of release from grief.

# Practice 21

# USING THE GROUND TO CONNECT TO THE RIB CAGE

YOU LIE ON THE GROUND with knees bent and feet flat on the floor. You try to make the pressure of both feet sinking into the ground equal.

You feel your pelvis on the ground and, once again, try to create equal pressure going down the left and right sides into the ground.

Now you roll your pelvis up and down on the ground, so you feel the curve of your lower back arch and flatten.

» Can you notice what this feels like and how the arch also raises up the bottom of the back of your rib cage?

Next, you bring your attention to your chest

103

and your breath. You take a nice deep breath in. As you inhale, you pull the muscles inside your chest (around your spine in your rib cage) slowly up towards your neck and your throat, as tight and as far up as you can contact them.

When you've pulled the muscles up as far as you can, you hold for the count of three, then release.

You slowly release the muscles, softening the area towards the base of your rib cage first, then letting the higher area follow.

» Can you feel how you're creating a much flatter arch in your back? Instead of simply tipping your rib cage upwards, using your pelvis, you draw it up and actively get into all the muscles, contracting and releasing.

» You have a flatter curve in your spine. However, can you feel that the arch travels further up the spine?

You repeat this practice as often as possible, as it helps to release all kinds of tension in your upper body.

SKETCH

>>→ Small movements lead to big shifts in alignment

✏ JOURNAL

# Practice 22
# Rib Cage in Sagittal Plane

You stand in front of a mirror and put your hands on the front of your chest.

You make sure your feet, pelvis and spine are in good alignment with the tripods of your feet well-connected with the ground.

Now, you have the intention of lifting the front of your rib cage upwards. This is a posterior rib cage tilt.

If this feels difficult, can you focus on your in-breath as it fills up your lungs? Can you feel how the rib cage naturally rises up with this? Can you then allow the movement to become a little bigger?

» Can you sense that the slower you take the in-breath, the more easily you will be able to connect with the movement of your muscles?

Now you focus on what happens with your out-breath as your rib cage sinks down.

As the rib cage softens, you allow your spine to soften and flex. You keep your eyes on the horizon so your rib cage moves away from your head, rather than your head and rib cage moving together with head lunging forwards.

» Is it more natural for your head to want to move with your rib cage?

Now you practice these movements together, moving from a posterior tilt of the rib cage back to neutral.

» Can you naturally move through this plane of movement? Or do you feel stuck at the base of your rib cage?
» Can you feel into the movement of your rib cage as it rises and sinks?

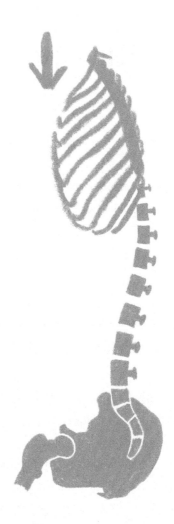

SKETCH ⮑

>>+ Small movements lead to big shifts in alignment ✦

# JOURNAL

# Practice 23

# RIB CAGE IN FRONTAL PLANE

YOU PUT YOUR HANDS ON YOUR CHEST and keep your head still, tilting your rib cage to the left and then to the right.

» Do your eyes stay on the horizon? Or is your head travelling sideways with your rib cage?

If your head is moving, you pick something on the horizon to fix your gaze on. Then keep your eyes there while you tilt your rib cage sideways.

To help with the tilt, when sending the right side of your rib cage upwards, you send the fingertips of your left hand downwards.

Or, if you're tilting the right side of your rib cage upwards, you gently raise your right arm upwards, and send your right-hand fingertips pointing upwards, but over your left ear. (You don't overstretch your shoulder, or cause discomfort, but you do fully extend your fingers as if to touch the ceiling.)

Now you repeat this on the other side.

You keep in mind that the movement is driven from the base of the rib cage, not pulled by the

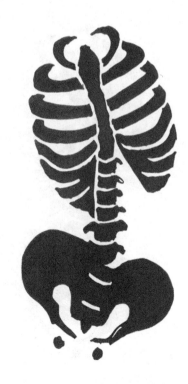

arm or shoulder going upwards.

» Is it easier to tilt left or right?
» Can you notice if one side of your rib cage is generally higher than the other?
» Does the base of your rib cage feel tighter on one side?

In frontal plane, you look for the top of your rib cage to tip up and down sideways like a seesaw.

You make sure your clavicle bones (the bones that sit between your throat and your shoulders) don't move individually, as this would move the

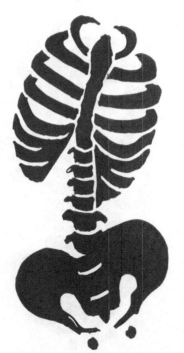

shoulder joint and hunch your shoulders.

» Do you find it difficult to see or understand the difference between moving the rib cage and shoulder?
» When you try to move your rib cage left or right, do you find your first physical response is to move your shoulder joint towards your ear?
» Can you see how this is not moving the rib cage?
» Can you compare the illustrations with your appearance in the mirror?

If there is a healthy gap between your ear and shoulder (ie. shoulder not hunched), then you know the shoulder is rising naturally along with the rib cage, instead of hunching upwards on its own.

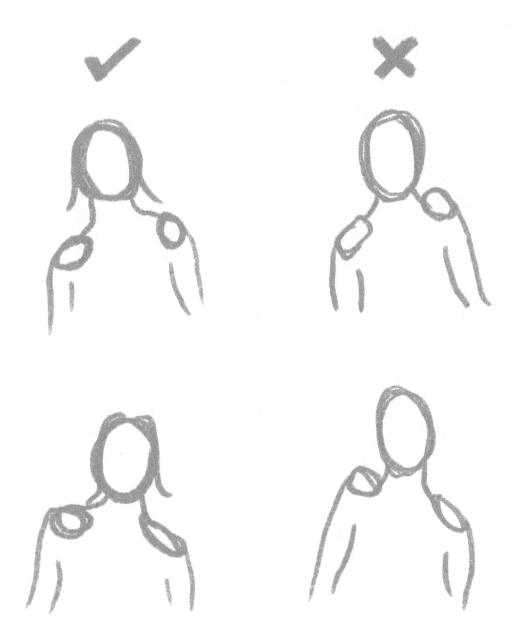

## SKETCH

➵ Small movements lead to big shifts in alignment ✒

✎ JOURNAL

_____

_____

_____

_____

_____

_____

_____

_____

_____

_____

_____

_____

_____

_____

_____

_____

_____

_____

_____

# Practice 24

# RIB CAGE IN TRANSVERSE PLANE

YOU STAND WITH YOUR FEET facing 12 o'clock and knees fully extended. You keep your rib cage directly above your pelvis and engage your hip flexors.

You rotate your rib cage towards 3 o'clock, but don't let your head, or pelvis, turn to 3 o'clock as well.

» Is it hard to isolate the movement of your rib cage from your head?

» What does the movement feel like in the middle of the back of your rib cage when you get towards 3 o'clock? Can you feel a twisting and contracting there?

Now you do the same movement, but allow your head to go with your rib cage.

» Can you feel how there is no contraction in your spine in the middle?

Now do the same on the other side towards 9 o'clock.

» Do you have more mobility going towards 3 o'clock or 9 o'clock?

» As you practice the art of getting good rotation in your spine and rib cage, are you able to:

» Anchor your pelvis facing forwards so it does not rotate with the rib cage?

» Keep your eyes on the horizon in front of you to anchor your head?

» Can you sense that, if you keep your head and your pelvis facing forwards, it creates an anchor so the muscles above and below your rib cage actually get to fully extend and release?

Sᴋᴇᴛᴄʜ ⇥

➤ Small movements lead to big shifts in alignment ↗

JOURNAL

# Practice 25

# RIB CAGE IN THE CLOCK FACE

YOU STAND IN THE CLOCK FACE so your feet, knees, hip flexors, pelvis, and spine are aligned.

You allow your pelvis to rotate towards 3 o'clock, as far as it can go before any part of the tripod of either of your feet wants to leave the ground.

» Can you feel a natural stop of your pelvis when your belly button faces towards about 1 o'clock?

» When you leave your pelvis at 1 o'clock, can you see if your spine and rib cage can rotate further towards 3 o'clock (always keeping your tripods firmly on the ground)?

When your rib cage comes to a natural stop, you bring up your right arm so it's 90 degrees from the side of your right thigh.

» Next, with your arm at 90 degrees and the palm of your hand facing the floor, directly in line with your thigh, is your rib cage now able to rotate a little bit further towards 4 or 5 o'clock?

When you reach a natural stop, you rotate your arm so that your thumb moves upwards and backwards. Your shoulder joint slightly rotates.

» Does your rib cage then go slightly further around the clock face?

» Can you feel your same-side shoulder blade contracting in the area between your spine?

» Can you see if you can really contract this area and feel your spine spiralling and engaging?

You slowly rotate your hand so your palm is again facing the ground. Then you rotate back to where you lifted your arm, and lower it from there.

You move your rib cage back above your pelvis, then bring your pelvis back to 12 o'clock.

Repeat this movement on the other side.

» Can you feel how each part of your upper body has the ability to increase the range of movement, and get into small joints, so that you can feel the spiraling of your muscles through your spine?

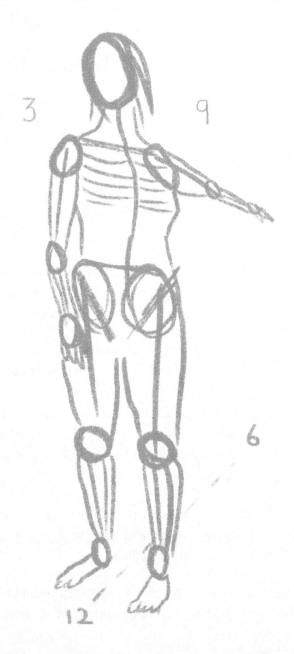

Sᴋᴇᴛᴄʜ

➤ Small movements lead to big shifts in alignment ✦

# MODULE 5
# Arms & Shoulders Unwound

'Sometimes, it's not the weight of what we carry that breaks us. It's the way we carry it.'

~ Brené Brown

YOU'RE FINALLY GOING TO LEARN how your shoulder blades and shoulder joints are completely different structures with completely different functions. As you learn to move each in isolation and to explore their precise ranges of movement, you'll begin to see how shoulder problems so easily arise. So long as the shoulder is moving as one fixed block, it lacks the integrity needed to bring safety and support to both the arm and the rib cage separately. As you learn to move your shoulder blades correctly, you will see how our earlier rib cage practices become so much easier and release can happen almost effortlessly.

**Can help solve:** frozen shoulder; rotator cuff injuries; carpal tunnel syndrome; arm problems; arthritis in the hands.

**Can help create:** a feeling of lightness and ease, especially for those stuck in 'helper mode' with the weight of the world on their shoulders.

## Practice 26

# FEELING YOUR SHOULDER BLADES (SCAPULAS)

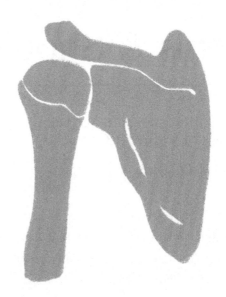

LYING DOWN, YOU LIFT YOUR RIB CAGE on the in-breath. Can you feel what happens to your shoulder blades?

Standing up, on the in-breath and on the out-breath, do you notice a difference in how much you can contract your shoulder blades based on what your breath is doing?

» Does it feel the same or different in the left and right shoulder?

You move your forearms in transverse, out to the sides.

» Do you have a sense of your shoulder blades?

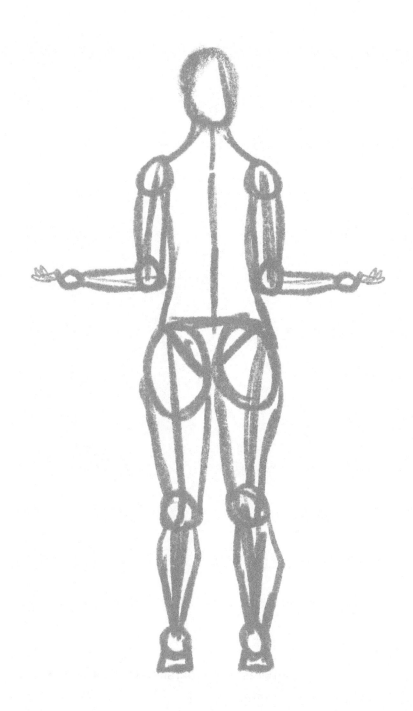

## SKETCH

➤ Small movements lead to big shifts in alignment ⌁

## ✎ JOURNAL

# Practice 27

# ROCKET ARMS

HOW FAR CAN YOUR ARMS go backwards above your head before your shoulders naturally reach the end of their movement range?

» Does it feel the same in your left and right shoulder?

» Look in the mirror – are your arms straight or bent? Can you fully extend your arms? How far can they go?

In this illustration, notice how one arm is straighter than the other. Are your arms different or the same?

Play with this movement in anterior pelvic tilt and then posterior.

» Can you feel a difference? Which feels better?

Play with doing this movement with your rib cage rising with the in-breath and sinking with the out-breath.

» What do you notice about your range of movement?

SKETCH ⇗

➤ Small movements lead to big shifts in alignment ↗

✏ JOURNAL

# Practice 28

# SEESAW SHOULDERS

WHEN YOUR ARMS REACH THE END of their range of movement above your head, what happens when your scapulas retract down and slightly inward, acting like the other end of a seesaw to draw your arms up?

» Does your range of movement increase?
» How does the range of motion change:

   » Moving from the shoulder joint?
   » Then from the scapula?
   » With rib cage raised on the in breath?
   » With rib cage sunk on the out breath?
   » With anterior pelvic tilt?
   » With posterior pelvic tilt?

» Does the smoothness or deepness of the movement change?
» What about with posterior pelvic tilt and hip flexors engaged?

## SKETCH ✍

➤ Small movements lead to big shifts in alignment ✒

✏️ JOURNAL

# Practice 29

# SHOULDERS AT 2 & 10 O'CLOCK

Y OU LEAD FROM THE SCAPULA to glide and pro-
tract your arms forward towards 2 and 10
o'clock (palms facing your thighs).

Now you slowly rotate at the wrists so your
thumbs turn inward towards your thighs.

You slowly unwind first the wrists, then the
shoulders and repeat the whole process.

»   Are you able to make the movement feel
    smooth and fluid?
»   Can you feel the distinct difference between
    the range of motion of your shoulder joint
    and scapula?

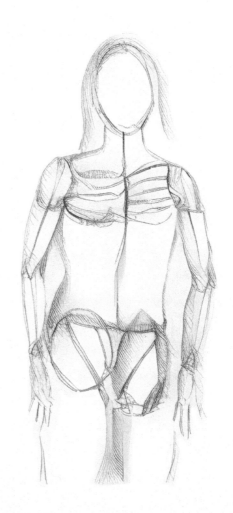

Sketch ⟳

➤ Small movements lead to big shifts in alignment ↗

✎  JOURNAL

# Practice 30

# SHOULDERS AT 4 & 8 O'CLOCK

Y OU LEAD FROM THE SCAPULAS to rotate your arms back towards 4 and 8 o'clock.

»   Can you feel the contraction in your upper back and the opening in the front of your chest?

»   When you rotate the wrists backwards, can you feel an added spreading and engagement of chest muscles and contraction at the scapulas?

You move in and out of this movement till it flows.

»   Does it feel the same on both sides? Is one side more restricted?

SKETCH ✑

≫→ Small movements lead to big shifts in alignment ✐

## ✏ JOURNAL

# Practice 31

# COMPLETE CLOCK FACE

YOU TAKE YOUR TIME to put the last two movements together, going forwards and backwards in the clock face.

» Did you let your joints and muscle fibres experience the movements slowly?

» Are you clear about the separate movements of the shoulder joint and the scapula?

» Will you try this process next time you're sitting at the computer for a long time?

This can help release upper body tension caused by repetitive strain.

Sketch ⟿

⇉ Small movements lead to big shifts in alignment ↗

JOURNAL

# Practice 32

# BICEPS, TRICEPS, HANDS & SHOULDER JOINTS

WITH ELBOWS GLUED TO THE SIDES of your rib cage (palms up as if holding a tray), you rotate your arms outward towards 3 and 9 o'clock.

Then you try completing that movement focusing on your biceps.

Now you try it while focusing on the area at the front of your shoulder joint at the top edge of your rib cage.

» Can you feel the big shift in movement when you change your focus?

» How do you feel, realising such a simple movement is improved, simply by changing where focus is applied?

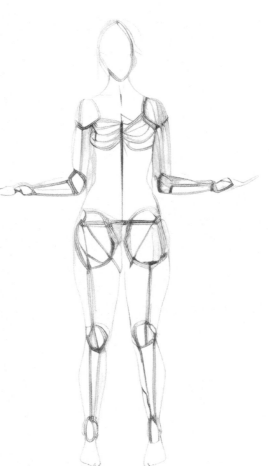

## Sketch ✍

>> Small movements lead to big shifts in alignment ✐

✏️ JOURNAL

# Practice 33

## CIRCUMDUCTION

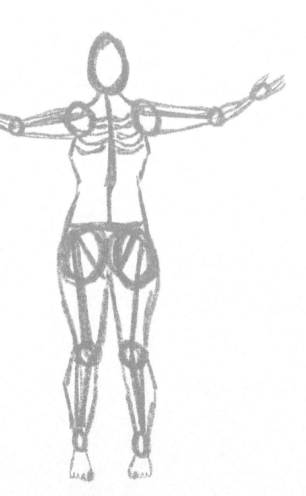

YOU REPEAT PRACTICE 28 (seesaw shoulders). When your arms are as high as they can go, you have your scapular to draw inward and downward, allowing your arms to come full circle behind you, down, back, and out slightly to the sides.

You explore your range of movement in this wheel-like motion.

» Is this simple or does it feel difficult to move from seesaw into a full circle?

This is a simple exercise to finish with, which brings all movements into your shoulders.

» Does one side have a different range of motion than the other?

SKETCH ✍

➤ Small movements lead to big shifts in alignment ↗

# MODULE 6
# The Neck Open & Shut

'Joints act; muscles react.'

~ Gary Ward

RELEASING NECK MUSCLES should never be done by manipulating the neck muscles themselves. Here you'll learn some incredible practices to release your neck by mobilising the skull, or the rib cage (each in isolation, in three planes of movement) or the skull and the rib cage together (moving in opposition). Never again will you roll your head in a circle!

Going forward, you'll understand how the the integrity of your skull movement, when it's neither collapsed forwards nor backwards, can completely transform pain in the upper body. The neck is a small area with many small structures inside it, so when you learn how to protect these structures correctly, everything from migraines to blood flow and shoulder problems can be relieved.

Can help solve: headaches; neck pain; throat tightness; breathing issues.

Can help create: greater capacity for communication and relaxed self-expression.

# Practice 34

## NECK IN SAGITTAL PLANE

YOU ROCK YOUR HEAD backwards and forwards slowly.

» Though this a regular daily movement, do you find it's easy for you to bring your chin forwards and down towards your chest?

» When you do this, do you feel like you've got something stuck in your throat?

» Does it feel squashed and uncomfortable in that area at the front of your neck? Or does it feel like you have plenty of space for movement?

» Do you get a nice opening at the back of your neck when you are sending your chin forwards and down towards your chest, or does it feel stretched and restricted at the back?

» When sending your head backwards, do you feel a pinch at the base of your skull? Or does it feel like a nice compression?

» What's the more enjoyable sensation, sending your chin downwards or the base of your skull backwards and downward?

While sitting down, you become aware of your hip flexors being at a 90-degree angle with your rib cage neutral above your pelvis.

» Does this feel normal?

» When you correct that posture, do you find you get a smoother movement

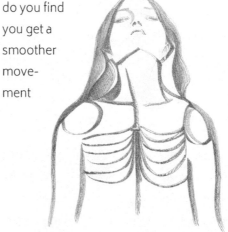

» at the back of the base of your skull?
» If the muscles in your neck are still quite tight, can you feel your whole body slightly bracing?

You resist the temptation to do the sagittal plane movement quickly. Instead you slow it down in order to gain more information.

Next, you stand up to do these movements.

» Does your neck feel the same in sagittal plane or different?

» How does it affect your neck if your hip flexors are not engaged compared to if they are engaged?
» What happens in your neck when you move your pelvis or your rib cage through these tilts?
» As you practice and feel the relationships between neck, pelvis and rib cage, what creates more tension? What creates ease and feels good to do?
» Can you sense that movement of the neck is different if you sit down and anchor it, compared to when you stand up?

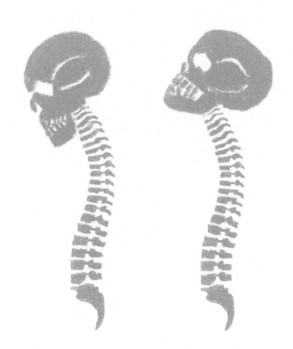

## SKETCH

➤ Small movements lead to big shifts in alignment ✎

✎ JOURNAL

# Practice 35

# Neck in Frontal Plane

To help make the movement accurate, you put your finger on the tip of your nose. Now you move your right ear towards your right shoulder and make sure your finger is not pushed down towards your chest (as this indicates you're slightly moving into sagittal and not just staying in frontal plane).

So, you simply move your nose on this axis. Your eyes stay looking forward.

» Do you find yourself looking towards the side of the room (instead of directly ahead)? If yes, that's a rotation mixed up with flexion, and you don't want that!

  » Do you find your eyes start travelling up? This is also rotation, so take care to keep your eyes looking at the horizon as your head tips to the side.

  » Can you feel your muscles immediately at the base of the skull? You're getting into the top cervical vertebrae (the bones in your neck), where the muscles connect the spine to the base of the skull.

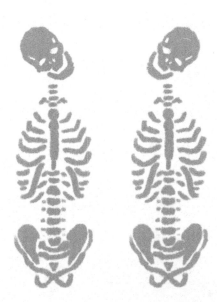

Now you do the same movement without your finger on your nose. Still, you keep your nose on the same axis.

» Do you find this helps you get lower down in terms of your neck muscles?
» Are you managing to not look down to-wards the floor, but simply side bend your neck with your ear going down to your shoulder?

If you're sitting, to make the move-ment stronger, you sit on the op-posite hand. So, if your left ear is going towards your left shoul-der, you sit on the palm of your right hand.

Now you repeat the whole process on the other side.

» Do you notice if it is different on each side?
» Is right or left easier for the frontal side bend?

» Do you find it's easier to maintain alignment if you film yourself or watch yourself in the mirror?

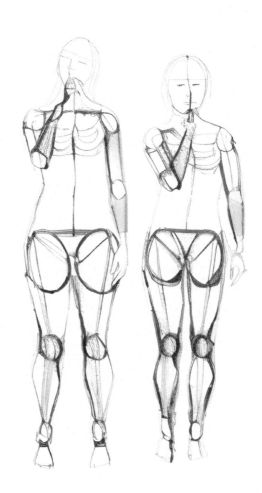

You need to take great care to follow the instructions for good alignment because the small muscles of the neck mean slight misalignments cause major pressure across muscle groups and joints so it's easy to make mistakes without realising.

You can try these movements sitting and standing.

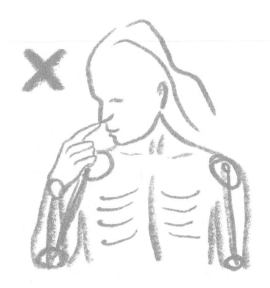

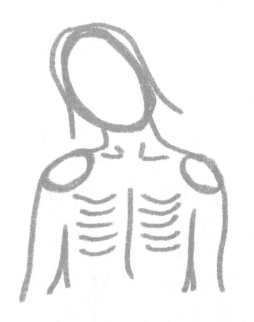

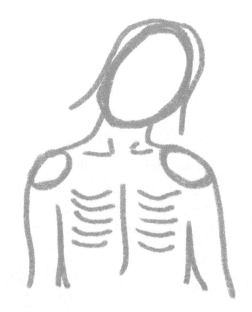

SKETCH

➤ Small movements lead to big shifts in alignment ✐

✎ JOURNAL

# Practice 36

# NECK IN TRANSVERSE PLANE

You sit in a chair and fix your eyes at horizon level. You rotate your head towards 3 o'clock.

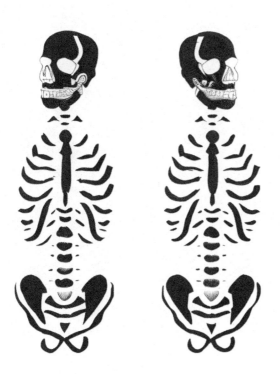

» How far can it go? Can you rotate your head without your nose wanting to dip downwards AT ALL?

Now you rotate your head towards 9 o'clock.

» How far can it go? Can you rotate your head without your nose wanting to dip downwards AT ALL?

Now repeat this process towards 3 and 9 o'clock with your rib cage lifting up with your breath.

» How does this impact your range of movement?

Now repeat the process, with your rib cage collapsed for the out-breath.

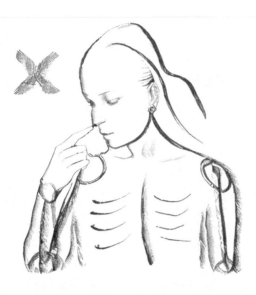

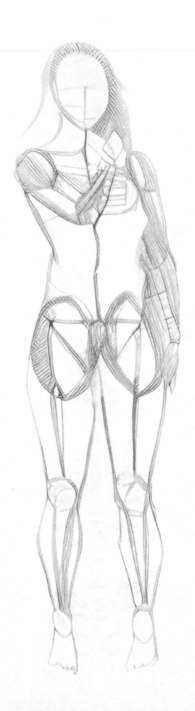

» What do you notice about your range of movement on either side of your neck?

Now do the above, but from a standing position, with your tripod and all other parts of your body correctly aligned.

» Do you feel a different connection with your neck when standing? If so, how does it show up for you?

» Can you feel how your neck problems may be due to tiny muscle misalignments?

SKETCH

➻ Small movements lead to big shifts in alignment ✐

JOURNAL

# Practice 37

# RIB CAGE RELIEF

THIS IS THE ULTIMATE HACK for getting into your neck muscles!

You look in the mirror at your clavicles and find the horizontal lines that connect the top of your arm to the dip below the front of your neck.

You want the line of the two clavicles to move like a seesaw. You don't want the shoulder joint to hunch up into the neck. You have already done this in practice 23.

Keeping your eyes on the horizon, you allow the top of your rib cage to sink sideways.

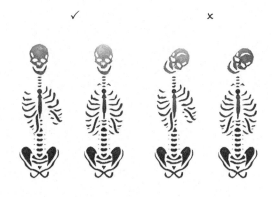

» Can you feel the deep stretch into your neck, without you moving your neck at all?

You repeat this on both sides a few times.

Checking in the mirror are you able to allow your clavicle bone to move through space, as your rib cage sinks, without the clavicle hunching upward?

On the downwards side, you put your intention into the fingertips. They actively point downwards, as if wanting to touch the floor.

On the downward side, you move your ear in frontal plane away from that shoulder.

» Can you feel that this gives an even **deeper** opening on that side of your neck?

You repeat this on the other side.

» Where do you feel restrictions?
» What feels good?
» What feels like you need to be careful?

You never overstretch, but simply work around the edge of your range of movement.

» Are you able to perform this movement from movement from your spine and sternum, at the centre of your chest (instead of from your shoulder joints)?
» Can you feel how keeping your neck still, but moving your rib cage, particularly in frontal plane, can give your neck a deep stretch, releasing it without your having to move your neck at all?
» Can you sense how this approach could release a sore neck far better than the method most people use, which is to stretch the sore area and aggravate their inflammation even more?

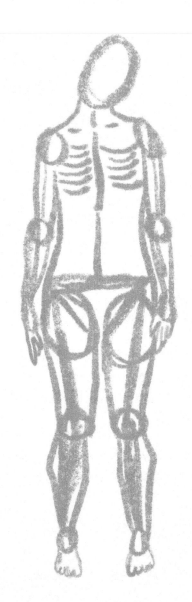

SKETCH

≫→ Small movements lead to big shifts in alignment ✎

JOURNAL

# Practice 38

# NECK IN THE CLOCK FACE

YOU ALIGN YOURSELF in the clock face facing 12 o'clock.

You move to rotate your neck so your eyes move around the clock face on the horizon toward 1-2 o'clock.

You drop your chin in the sagittal plane, down towards your chest.

Now you take your 3 o'clock arm forwards to a 90-degree angle from your chest with your fingers pointing to 12 o'clock.

You allow the 9 o'clock side of your rib cage to drop down so your left-hand fingers are fully engaged and pointing down to the floor.

» What is happening in your neck now?
» Can you feel how, when we introduce sagittal, frontal and transverse plane in the clock face, you get a profound neck release?

You repeat this on the other side. Due to the technicality of this movement, here's the process again:

You rotate your neck towards 10 - 11 o'clock.

You drop your chin down in sagittal plane, towards your chest.

You take your 9 o'clock arm forward raised at an angle of 90 degrees from your chest.

You point the fingers fully engaged towards 12 o'clock.

Now you let the 3 o'clock side of your rib cage sink down with fingers fully engaged and pointing to the floor.

You experiment with swapping which arm is forward and which arm is downwards while keeping your neck in the same position.

» Can you understand why simply rolling your shoulders, or sending your head in one direction, has not been the ticket to release your neck pain?

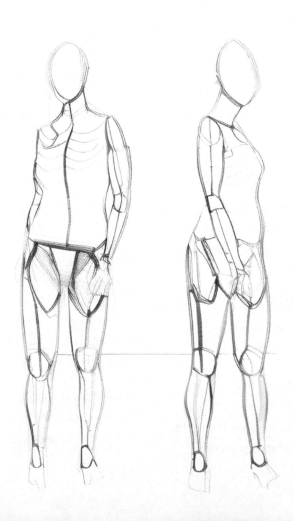

✏️ SKETCH

➤ Small movements lead to big shifts in alignment ✒️

✏ JOURNAL

# Practice 39

# NECK IN SUSPENSION & PROPULSION

YOU PUT YOURSELF into the left leg (front leg forward) suspension position in the clock face, as per practice 13.

You put your pelvis correctly into a sagittal, frontal and transverse plane, so your direction is towards 1 o'clock.

You turn your rib cage to 11 o'clock. In sagittal plane, your rib cage is lifted. In frontal plane, the left side of your rib cage seesaws down towards your forward left leg. In transverse plane, your rib cage goes towards 11 o'clock as your pelvis goes towards 1 o'clock.

Now you bring your attention to your head and skull. You take your left arm backwards and downwards with fingers pointing to the floor, while taking your right ear towards your right shoulder at 90 degrees.

You move slowly in and out of this movement.

» How does it feel in your neck, as your whole body moves? Can you feel the contraction in your neck?

Now you do the same movement, but this time you take your left arm forward (instead of downward) along with your left leg. With your right ear going to the right shoulder, you let the back of your skull and head lift upwards.

Now you repeat this with your right leg forward, which requires your pelvis to face 11 o'clock, your rib cage to 1 o'clock, and your left ear towards your left shoulder.

As you do these movements, you bring your back leg into propulsion. You try the movements with your back foot correctly in supination with hip, knee and ankle rotating away. You make sure your fifth met stays connected throughout.

You compare this to when you keep the back leg heel and whole tripod on the ground. What do you notice in your neck, depending on the placement of your back foot?

» Can you feel how movement of the rest of your body is able to bring full engagement, both for contraction and release, into the muscles of your neck?

SKETCH ✍

➤ Small movements lead to big shifts in alignment ✒

# Module 7
# The Jaw & the Breath

'The time it takes to establish a sense of calm is time well spent.'
~ Peter A. Levine

THE JAW IS A FASCINATING PART of the body in terms of its connection with the skull as part of the spine: if you imagine the full length of your spine, with skull at one end and pelvis at the other – when the jaw is locked, it can restrict movement in areas at the very far end of the body.

So, as we come to the jaw practices, we put everything we've learned so far together. If jaw tension can lock up every other joint in your body then, when we relax the jaw and bring consciousness to this area, it has the power to release shoulders, rib cage and even the pelvis.

So, after this module, why not revisit earlier practices, with your new understanding, to see if you get a different experience?

**Can help solve:** headaches; jaw pain.

**Can help create:** effortless; buoyant gait with engaged experience of presence and capacity for softness instead of feeling stuck; tight; contracted.

## Practice 40

# RETRACTION & PROTRACTION

Y OU SEND THE BOTTOM OF YOUR JAW forwards (protraction). You draw it back (retraction).

» Does it feel awkward (since this is an un-common movement)?

» Does it get easier with time?

Now you repeat protraction with attention on the area of your jaw directly in front of your ears.

Now you repeat retraction drawing in from your chin.

Next you repeat retraction with focus on the joint of the upper and lower jaw in front of your ears.

» What difference do you notice when you experiment with the different movements?

SKETCH

➤ Small movements lead to big shifts in alignment ✦

✎　JOURNAL

# Practice 41

# JAW MOVING SIDE TO SIDE IN FRONTAL PLANE

YOU SEND THE JAW TO EACH SIDE in the frontal plane.

» Does one side feel easier than the other?
» Where else in your skull do you feel pressure and contraction when you do this?

You repeat the practice with your mouth open, then with your mouth nearly shut. Then with head rotated towards 3 o'clock, then towards 9 o'clock.

» Does it feel the same, easier or more restricted?

## Sᴋᴇᴛᴄʜ

➻ Small movements lead to big shifts in alignment ↗

JOURNAL

# Practice 42

# OPEN WIDE, CLENCH SHUT

OPEN YOUR MOUTH as wide as you can.

» Do you feel a restriction around your jaw joint in front of your ear?

» Does it feel scary to open your mouth that wide, or is it nice and relaxed?

» Does this feel familiar or difficult to do?

» Can you feel the tension in the rest of your body when you do it?

You move between opening wide and clenching tight.

» How does this feel in the back of your skull and your neck?

» Can you feel the impact on deeper muscles in your throat and chest?

Sᴋᴇᴛᴄʜ ⇝

➠ Small movements lead to big shifts in alignment ↗

JOURNAL

# Practice 43

# JAW & THE BREATH

YOU SIT AND DON'T DO ANYTHING special with your jaw.

» How does your jaw align naturally?

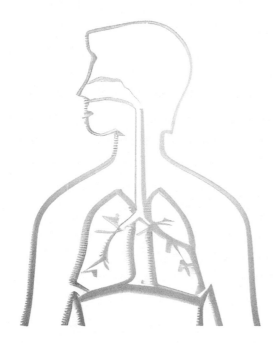

You relax your jaw and take a breath with your mouth open.

» What happens when your jaw relaxes and you breath in?
» What do you notice about your pelvis?
» What do you notice about your feet?

You stand up in correct alignment and breath with a relaxed jaw.

» Do you notice a difference compared to when you were sitting?
» What about in your pelvis and feet?
» Can you feel a different connection with your feet when you breath in, then out, with an open jaw, rather than nasal breathing?
» Is it difficult to keep your jaw soft and relaxed?

## SKETCH ✍

⇒ Small movements lead to big shifts in alignment ✒

✏️ JOURNAL

# Practice 44

# JAW SCAN WHILE SITTING

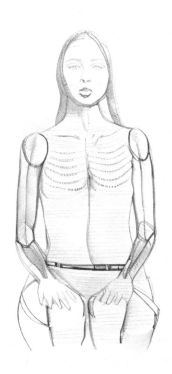

YOU SIT ON A CHAIR with feet hip-width apart, flat on the floor, knees at a 90-degree angle or more and take a few normal breaths.

You relax your jaw and allow your rib cage to rise and settle with the breath.

» How does your rib cage mobility feel with your jaw relaxed?

You allow your pelvis to anterior tilt on the in-breath and posterior tilt on the out-breath.

» Do you have a connection with your feet?

You repeat all the above movements but with a clenched, tight, shut mouth.

» What is the difference?
» Can you feel tension in your jaw restricting movement in your muscles and joints?

## SKETCH ⟳

➤ Small movements lead to big shifts in alignment ✦

✎ JOURNAL

# Practice 45

# JAW SCAN WHILE STANDING

YOU STAND UP with feet hip-width apart. Your feet, legs, pelvis, spine, and rib cage are nicely aligned. You take a few normal breaths.

Relax your jaw and let your rib cage rise and settle with each breath.

» How does the mobility feel in your rib cage and chest with jaw relaxed?
» Does it feel the same or different from when you were sitting down?
» You allow your pelvis to anterior tilt on the in-breath and exterior tilt on the out-breath.
» Do you have a connection with your feet?

You repeat all the above movements but with a clenched, tight, shut mouth.

» What is the difference?
» Can you feel tension in your jaw restricting movement in your muscles and joints?
» How far down your body does the impact go?
» Can you feel it just in your upper body, or as far down as your feet?

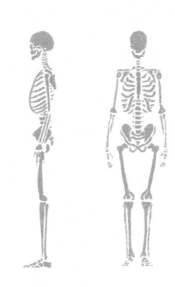

## SKETCH

→ Small movements lead to big shifts in alignment

✏ JOURNAL

# Practice 46

# CLENCHING & RELEASING THE JAW THROUGH THE CLOCK FACE

YOU STAND IN GOOD ALIGNMENT in the clock face. You move towards 3 o'clock, then 9 o'clock, with your jaw in your own version of neutral.

» Can you move more easily in one direction than the other?

You try the same movement with clenched jaw.

» Can you notice any difference in how far you can rotate around the clock face?

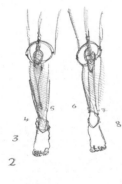

» Is it easier to go in one direction than the other?

Now you repeat the movement to 3 and 9 o'clock but with an open, relaxed jaw.

» Can you notice the difference in your mobility?

You practice the movement with your jaw relaxed and scan through the different joints in your body.

» How does each part of your body feel with a relaxed jaw?
» Can you feel how gravity sinks through your body when you relax your jaw?
» Can you try to recreate this in daily life?
» Overall, can you feel how the slightest jaw engagement has a full-body knock-on effect?
» Overall, can you feel this body–jaw association strongly or is your sense of it still quite weak?

Over time, can you feel how the more you explore these connections, the greater your capacity to release stiffness and pain?

SKETCH ✍

Small movements lead to big shifts in alignment ✒

JOURNAL

# Practice 47

# JAW & SUSPENSION

YOU PUT YOURSELF into left leg suspension (front leg forward) in the clock face (same as practice 13).

You put your pelvis correctly into a sagittal, frontal and transverse plane, so your direction is towards 1 o'clock.

Your rib cage faces 11 o'clock. It's lifted in the sagittal plane. The left side of your rib cage see-saws down towards the left leg that's forward. In the transverse plane, your rib cage goes towards 11 o'clock as your pelvis goes towards 1 o'clock.

You tense your jaw and move slowly in and out of the suspension movement.

» How does it feel in your neck, rib cage and the rest of your body?
» Can you feel the contraction or jittery movement?
» Could this be normal for you?

You repeat the movement with a relaxed, open jaw. You breathe in as you sink into the front leg and breath out as you come back to neutral.

You repeat this with your right leg forward, which will require your pelvis to face towards 11 o'clock and rib cage towards 1 o'clock.

» Can you feel the connection?
» Can you feel how gravity is helped or hindered in your body, depending on what is happening with your jaw?

# Sketch ⇛

➤ Small movements lead to big shifts in alignment ✦

✏️ JOURNAL

# Practice 48
# JAW & PROPULSION

YOU PUT YOURSELF into left leg suspension in the clock face.

You put your pelvis correctly into a sagittal, frontal and transverse plane, so your direction is towards 1 o'clock.

Your rib cage faces 11 o'clock. It's lifted in the sagittal plane. The left side of your rib cage see-saws down towards the left leg that's forward. In the transverse plane, your rib cage goes towards 11 o'clock as your pelvis goes towards 1 o'clock.

You test this front-leg arm stretching backwards or downwards and your back-leg arm stretching forwards or upwards.

You feel into bringing your back heel off the ground, while keeping the connection of first and fifth met.

» How does it feel when you do this with a clenched jaw?
» How does it feel with a relaxed, open jaw?

You bring your heel off the ground with the in-breath and return it to the ground with the out-breath.

» How does this feel with a tightly clenched jaw?
» How does it feel with a relaxed, open jaw?
» Can you feel a difference in the ease of propulsion based on the connection with the jaw? Or does it feel the same?

SKETCH ⇗

➤ Small movements lead to big shifts in alignment ⤤

# Conclusion

YOU DID IT. Congratulations on completing Get Into Your Body Level 1!

You've come so far – but the journey never ends. Keep running through these practices and bringing awareness into your body.

Remember, now you're part of the **Ixchel** community and I'd love for you to keep dropping into Zoom classes to get feedback on your movement.

You've begun to stabilise and realign your structure. You've begun to feel a sense of power, safety and belonging in your body.

Now, the work is to integrate this wisdom into the movements of your daily life.

With that goal in mind, consider joining us for **Get Into Your Body 2** which explores the timing and alignment of your joints and internal structures in the course of daily movements .

You're also welcome to visit us for a live session in Brighton or on one of our retreats where the in-person assessments can be even more powerful. I'd love the chance to meet you in person and celebrate your journey of discovery so far as you continue to light up your body with new awareness and securely and consciously put one foot in front of the other.

# APPENDIX

# The Ten Considerations

For each practice, reflect on these questions by Chris Sritharan:

1. What **should** this structure be able to do?

2. What **does** it do?

3. What do I need to restore?

4. How do I go about restoring movement that is not available?

5. When do I need that movement to happen?

6. What is particularly important about that movement for my body?

7. Do I know what that movement looks like?

8. Do I know what that movement feels like?

9. How do I work with this?

10. How am I going to measure my results?

**Note:** Chris is an outstanding bodywork practitioner who trained me on Gary Ward's excellent **Anatomy in Motion (AiM)** programme. AiM is a huge inspiration behind the development of **The Ixchel System**. If you get the opportunity to train with either of these two pioneering teachers, I recommend you jump at the chance.

Chris Sritharam: christopher-sritharan.com

Gary Ward: findingcentre.co.uk

# INSPIRATION FOR JOURNALLING

OLD:

PATTERNS

FEELING IN THE BODY

KINDS OF ACTIVITIES & BEHAVIOURS

ALIGNMENT

EXPERIENCE

NEW:

POSSIBILITY

EXPLORATION

RANGE OF MOVEMENT

SENSATIONS

EXPERIENCES

BEHAVIOURS

ALIGNMENT

**BEFORE:**

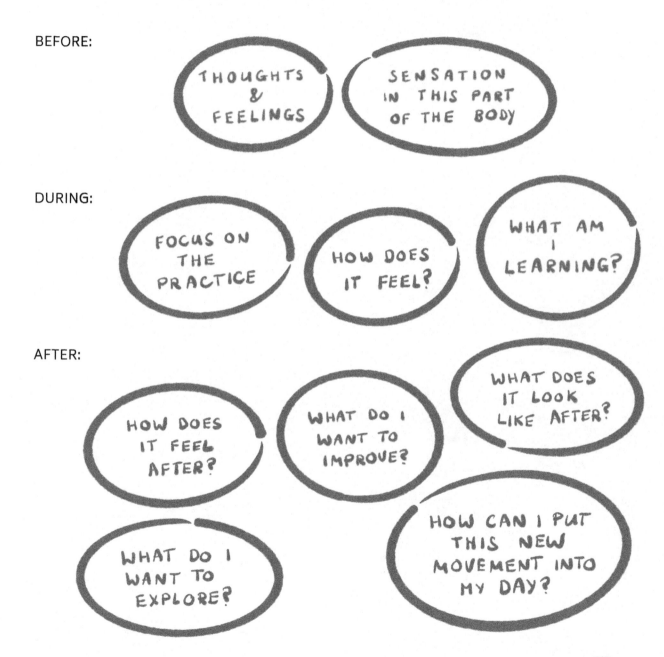

THOUGHTS & FEELINGS

SENSATION IN THIS PART OF THE BODY

**DURING:**

FOCUS ON THE PRACTICE

HOW DOES IT FEEL?

WHAT AM I LEARNING?

**AFTER:**

HOW DOES IT FEEL AFTER?

WHAT DO I WANT TO IMPROVE?

WHAT DOES IT LOOK LIKE AFTER?

WHAT DO I WANT TO EXPLORE?

HOW CAN I PUT THIS NEW MOVEMENT INTO MY DAY?

# INSPIRATION FOR SKETCHING

Mark areas of pressure or pain

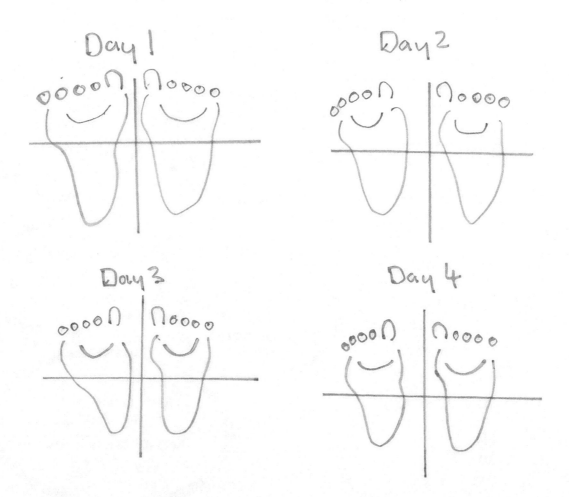

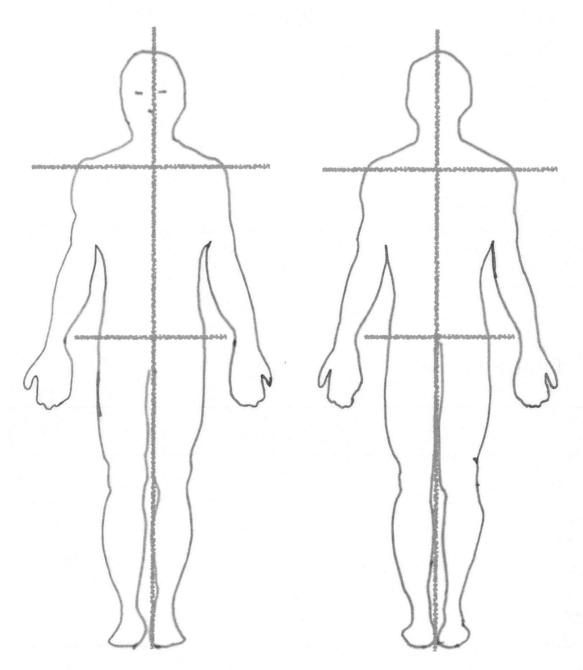

# MISALIGNMENT TRACKING TABLES

FROM FEET TO SKULL, use these tables to record your misalignment insights across time.

»   Enter the date up top
»   ✓   the box that matches your posture misalignment that day
»   X   the box that doesn't

## Feet Posture

| DATE | | | | | | | | | | | | | |
|------|---|---|---|---|---|---|---|---|---|---|---|---|---|
| Lower arched on left | | | | | | | | | | | | | |
| Lower arched on right | | | | | | | | | | | | | |
| Turned out more on left | | | | | | | | | | | | | |
| Turned out more on right | | | | | | | | | | | | | |

## Pelvic Posture

| DATE | | | | | | | | | | | | |
|---|---|---|---|---|---|---|---|---|---|---|---|---|
| Anterior tilt (forwards) | | | | | | | | | | | | |
| Posterior tilt (backwards) | | | | | | | | | | | | |
| Hike on left | | | | | | | | | | | | |
| Hike on right | | | | | | | | | | | | |
| Shifted to left | | | | | | | | | | | | |
| Shifted to right | | | | | | | | | | | | |
| Rotated to left | | | | | | | | | | | | |
| Rotated to right | | | | | | | | | | | | |

# Rib Cage Posture

| DATE | | | | | | | | | | | | |
|---|---|---|---|---|---|---|---|---|---|---|---|---|
| Anterior tilt (forwards) | | | | | | | | | | | | |
| Posterior tilt (backwards) | | | | | | | | | | | | |
| Sidebend left | | | | | | | | | | | | |
| Sidebend right | | | | | | | | | | | | |
| Rotated to left | | | | | | | | | | | | |
| Rotated to right | | | | | | | | | | | | |

# Shoulder Posture

| DATE | | | | | | | | | | | | |
|---|---|---|---|---|---|---|---|---|---|---|---|---|
| High on left | | | | | | | | | | | | |
| High on right | | | | | | | | | | | | |

# Skull Posture

| DATE | | | | | | | | | | | | |
|---|---|---|---|---|---|---|---|---|---|---|---|---|
| Anterior tilt (forwards) | | | | | | | | | | | | |
| Posterior tilt (backwards) | | | | | | | | | | | | |
| Sidebend left | | | | | | | | | | | | |
| Sidebend right | | | | | | | | | | | | |
| Rotated to left | | | | | | | | | | | | |
| Rotated to right | | | | | | | | | | | | |

# Do You Need Wedges?

A S YOU MOVE through Module 1, do you find it difficult to spread your weight evenly across the foot tripod without straining your feet?

If so, try putting a thin piece of cloth, like a thin sock, under the edge of first of fifth met.

If you find that's helping, I advise you invest in a tool called foot wedges, which you can insert under each foot while you practise Ixchel.

Scan the QR code above to visit Gary Ward's website and pick up a set. These will give your feet the support they need and allow your foot to slowly become used to distributing weight evenly.

After a few weeks or months of practising with wedges, your body should have adapted to a more balanced weight distribution and you should be able to practise strain-free without wedges.

If you're not sure, book a session with one of our practitioners for a personalised assessment:

IxchelTherapies.co.uk/one-to-one-session

# Whole Body Review

---

YOUR AMAZING BODY is an interconnected system so, each time you review a practice, even though your focus might be on the pelvis or the scapula alone, take a moment to make sure your whole body posture is aligned.

## FEET

» Is your weight balanced across the foot tripod?

» Do your second toes point to 12 o'clock?

## PELVIS

» Is your pelvis neutral (not tilted overly anterior or posterior in sagittal plane)?

## HIP FLEXORS

» Is your psoas engaged?

## SHOULDER

» Are your shoulders relaxed, not bunched up around your ears?

## JAW

» Is your jaw relaxed and loose?

## EVERYTHING

» Is your head stacked above your rib cage, stacked above your pelvis?

# The 48 Practices

# All in one place to refresh your memory

Made in the USA
Las Vegas, NV
13 January 2024

84321257R00122